C000242341

The Railwayman's Diesel Manual
(FOURTH EDITION)

A practical introduction to the diesel-powered
locomotive, railcar and multiple-unit train for
railway staff and railway enthusiasts

WILLIAM F. BOLTON
M.I.R.T.E., A.M.I.LOCO.E., M.S.A.E.

Ian Allan
PUBLISHING

First published 1956
Reprinted 1957 and 1958
Second edition 1958
Reprinted 1959
Third edition 1960
Fourth edition 1963
This impression 2006

ISBN (10) 0 7110 3197 5
ISBN (13) 978 0 7110 3197 5

© Ian Allan Publishing Ltd 1963

Published by Ian Allan Publishing

an imprint of Ian Allan Publishing Ltd, Hersham, Surrey KT12 4RG.
Printed by Ian Allan Printing Ltd, Hersham, Surrey KT12 4RG.

Code: 0608/B

THE AUTHOR AND PUBLISHERS wish to record their appreciation of the assistance afforded by Beyer-Peacock (Hymek) Ltd., Bristol Siddeley Engines Ltd., British United Traction Ltd., C.A.V. Ltd., Clayton Dewandre Co. Ltd., Davey, Paxman & Co. Ltd., Davies & Metcalfe Ltd., The English Electric Co. Ltd., Fluidrive Engineering Co. Ltd., Gresham & Craven Ltd., North British Locomotive Co. Ltd., Rolls-Royce Ltd., Self-Changing Gears Ltd., Serck Radiators Ltd., J. Stone & Co. (Deptford) Ltd., Sulzer Bros., and Westinghouse Brake & Signal Co. Ltd.

CONTENTS

6

CHAPTER ONE

THE DIESEL ENGINE
FUEL, AIR AND COMBUSTION

THE TERM "COMBUSTION" is employed to describe the burning of fuel in air, which is in fact a chemical reaction. An Internal Combustion engine is one which burns its fuel within the cylinders. Gas, Petrol and Diesel engines all come within this category. The steam locomotive is an example of the External Combustion engine in which the fuel is burned *outside* the cylinders.

Many persons confuse the abbreviation "i.c. engine" with "c.i. engine." The c.i. engine, or to give it its full title—the compression-ignition engine, is one in which the only source of fuel ignition is the heat generated by compression of air. The petrol engine in the popular form that we know today is an example of an internal combustion engine but it is not a c.i. engine, being in fact, a spark-ignition type.

Although it is in general use and has come to stay, the term "diesel" is not strictly correct and the description "compression-ignition oil engine" is more accurate. History reveals that Dr. Rudolph Diesel was not the pioneer of the particular type of engine so widely employed today in the road, rail, agricultural, marine and industrial fields, and true diesel engines are those which utilise blast-air injection. These today are largely obsolete.

It is invariably difficult to pinpoint the origin of any major invention but one pioneer of the compression-ignition oil engine we know today was James Ackroyd Stuart, a Scotsman who worked in England and took out patents in the years 1886-90. This was six years before Dr. Diesel's own patents, which although employing the main feature of compression-ignition, were based on the use of a fuel which consisted of a mixture of coal dust and oil blown into the cylinders through the medium of an air blast. A popular misconception is that diesels operate on a heavy crude oil of the type used for burning in oil-fired boilers of ships and locomotives. Crude oil is oil as it is extracted from the earth.

The fuel used in c.i. engines is a high ignition quality distillate fuel which ignites directly by the heat of air compression. When it leaves the refinery it is free from foreign solid matter which would for instance be found in crude oil.

Diesel fuel is less fluid and less readily evaporated than petrol. It is less likely to form an explosive mixture if accidentally spilled. The British Standards Specification 2869/1957 prescribes a minimum flash point of 130 degrees Fahrenheit, determined by the Pensky Martin closed cup method.

AIR-28.lbs.

Fig. 2.
Diesel engine
fuel-air ratio.
(The black portion
represents one pound
of fuel oil.)

Chemically, diesel fuel is composed of a particular range of the family of hydrocarbons; in other words it consists of carbon and hydrogen combined together in a particular form. On combustion, energy is generated which is used in the engine and the reaction of the fuel molecule with oxygen in the air creates carbon dioxide and water as waste products; the water of course passes from the exhaust as steam.

To successfully burn the fuel we require the addition of oxygen. Air—which contains one part of oxygen to four parts nitrogen, provides this essential gas. In order to burn one pound of diesel oil approximately 28 pounds of air are required and this is obtained from the charge of clean air which, as will be seen later, is highly compressed within the combustion chambers of the diesel engine.

The flow characteristics of diesel fuel are measured in a viscometer through the medium of which we are enabled to discover the number of seconds a given quantity of oil will take to flow through a measured orifice. Imagine a container which is equipped at its tapered base with a small opening and valve, this receptacle is filled with oil to a definite level mark, after which the valve is opened and the oil allowed to flow out. The number of seconds taken to completely empty the measured amount of oil through the orifice is the oil's viscosity. At 100 degrees Fahrenheit, using the commonly employed Redwood No. 1 Viscometer, it is found that modern diesel fuel gives a reading of approximately 34 seconds. For comparison, the lubricating oils used in modern internal combustion engines have an average viscosity of 480 seconds at 100 degrees Fahrenheit.

Diesel fuel is not likely to explode or ignite in bulk, neither is it likely to catch fire and it is as a result of this considerable margin of safety over the spark-ignition or petrol engine that the diesel has several times been applied to aircraft. Because of its relatively high flash point diesel fuel is less likely to form an inflammable vapour than petrol. Nevertheless there is always a potential danger and therefore a spark or burning match might quite likely cause a serious fire in the storage area.

Any place where diesel oil vapour may collect *in a confined area* is potentially dangerous and under no circumstances should any person be permitted to use a naked flame (flare-lamp, candle, wax-taper, etc.) within the vicinity of the storage tanks, irrespective of whether they be attached to the vehicle or stationary. The same warning applies where fuel oil hoses and pipes are concerned and, in connection with refuelling generally. The vent pipes from fuel oil tanks should be inspected frequently to ensure that they are clear of obstructions.

These points should be firmly impressed in the minds of all who have dealings with diesel-powered locomotives and railcars.

COMBUSTION

The term compression-ignition is self explanatory but briefly speaking, in order to ensure that the fuel is ignited in the combustion chamber, inducted air must be compressed to approximately 500 lbs. per square inch in which state the resultant temperature is between 800 and 1,000 degrees Fahrenheit. (In a petrol engine an electric spark sets the fuel mixture on fire when compression has taken place up to approximately 125 lbs. per square inch only, and resulting burning creates a rise in pressure which drives the piston downwards.) In the diesel the fuel oil begins burning the moment it comes into contact with the hot air and slowly becomes fully burned, thus a gradual increase in pressure is created within the combustion chamber, resulting in an almost constant pressure on the piston. The diesel is therefore often referred to as a "constant pressure engine."

The ratio of compression of modern high speed diesel engines averages 17 to 1 compared with an average of only 6 to 1 with modern transport petrol engines, and it will be readily appreciated that diesel engine components must be considerably more robust than those associated with spark-ignition units. This particularly applies to the design of the connecting rods, crankshaft and main bearings, and we shall deal with this subject in some detail later.

Various means are employed to ensure thorough combustion of the fuel and a high degree of atomisation. Among these can be mentioned specially-shaped combustion chambers situated in the piston crown or cylinder head and " masked " inlet valves, all of which help to promote air swirl. In addition, the piston itself is brought extremely close to the cylinder head when at top-dead-centre (see Chapter Two) the minimum clearance being as small as $\frac{3}{64}$ of an inch, creating a secondary movement of the air from around the outer portion of the piston crown into the combustion chamber itself. This movement of the air is known to c.i. engine designers as "squish."

As mentioned already, the fuel-oil on entering the combustion chamber ignites and "slowly" becomes fully burned. It is commonly thought that ignition takes place the instant the fuel hits the highly heated air charge, but this is not so and there is a definite delay, termed "ignition lag," which, according to type of combustion chamber, may last from 15 to 45° of crank angle. If the major portion of the fuel charge is already within the cylinder when ignition occurs it will ignite almost instantaneously and explode with considerable violence. This explosion is known as combustion-knock or, more popularly, "diesel knock." In well-designed engines diesel knock has been greatly reduced over the last two decades.

CHAPTER TWO

THE DIESEL ENGINE

OPERATING CYCLES

THE CYCLE OF OPERATIONS of a diesel engine varies according to type. The type most common in Britain is known as the Four-stroke Single-Acting. It was upon the Four-stroke cycle that most of the original compression-ignition engine designs were evolved.

In 1890 Ackroyd-Stuart built his first compression-ignition engine, working with a compression pressure of under 100 pounds per square inch, and it was a Four-stroke horizontal design of the "hot bulb" type, the term applied to those engines which obtain their heat for starting from external sources—such as a flame from a blow lamp directed against the outside walls of the combustion chamber. Nevertheless, the Ackroyd-Stuart design of 1890 had an injection pump of the mechanical type, which was the direct ancestor of today's injection pump. This method of injection by a mechanical pressure pump is referred to as the "solid injection" method. It should not be forgotten, however, that William Priestman, working on similar lines, patented a compression-ignition engine as early as 1885, together with many other systems. The invention of the practical steam locomotive is rarely credited to the pioneering genius of Richard Trevithick, similarly, the c.i. engine pioneer, Ackroyd-Stuart rarely received credit for its origin.

The diesel engine proper, of which there are still some in commercial use, employs a blast of air to deliver the fuel into the cylinder, instead of a mechanical pump. The author whilst employed as an engineer on a 12,000 tons motor ship undertook the operation and the maintenance of two 8,000 b.h.p. true diesel engines.

In describing the various operating cycles which follow, it should be noted that for the sake of simplicity, single-cylinder engines only are being described.

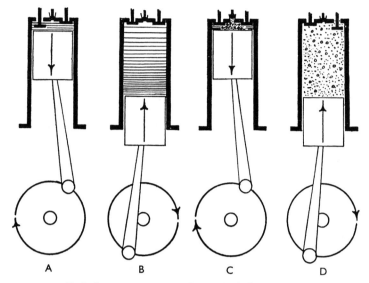

Fig. 3. Sequence of operations. Four-stroke single-acting engine.

FOUR-STROKE SINGLE-ACTING (*See Fig. 3 above*)

With this type of engine the cycle of operations is as follows:—the piston, moving downwards in the cylinder from top-dead-centre (A) creates a suction which causes freshly filtered air to be drawn through the open inlet valve. It is of importance to note that, unlike the petrol engine, only *air* passes the inlet valve. Reaching bottom-dead-centre the piston commences to rise (B) and, as the inlet valve closes, the trapped air is compressed to approximately 500 lbs. per square inch.

Towards the end of the stroke and some few degrees before t.d.c. the injection of fuel commences and continues for about 20 to 24 degrees of crankshaft rotation. With an engine running at 1,500 revolutions per minute this action takes place in one 200th of a second! The temperature of the compressed air at the time of fuel injection is in the neighbourhood of 1,000 degrees Fahrenheit, resulting in instantaneous burning of the oil following which the pressure within the cylinder immediately rises by some 300 lbs. per square inch, driving the piston downwards on the third or working stroke (C).

Passing b.d.c. the exhaust valve opens (D) and the rising piston forces the burnt gases out of the cylinder. The cycle of operations is then complete and the four-stroke single-acting engine has therefore, one power stroke in every two revolutions.

The induction of air (A) and the disposal of the exhaust gases (D) may be assisted in some designs by means of a low-pressure blast of air, a mild form of supercharging known as " scavenging." On the other hand high-pressure air may be applied for full supercharging—the two systems should not be confused. Engines which draw in air by suction only and therefore breathe without the assistance of scavenge pumps or pressure-chargers are known as "normally aspirated."

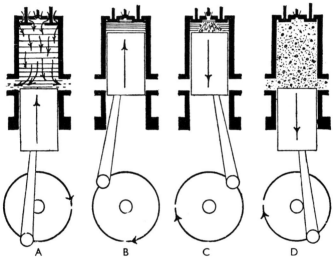

Fig. 4. Sequence of operations. Two-stroke single-acting engine.

TWO-STROKE SINGLE-ACTING (*See Fig.* 4 *above*)

Commencing with the piston at b.d.c. the air is admitted under pressure through twin inlet valves (A) and the piston commences to rise, causing the air to be compressed as the valves in the cylinder head are closed (B). Shortly before t.d.c. the fuel is injected, combustion takes place, and the piston then begins to descend on the downward or power stroke (C). Towards the end of this stroke the exhaust ports situated in the walls of the cylinder are uncovered by the piston and the exhaust gases thus released (D). Shortly afterwards the air inlet valves in the cylinder head are opened and clean air scavenges the cylinder (A)—the engine is now ready to commence another cycle of operations.

It will be observed with the two-stroke engine that every downward stroke of the piston is a power stroke. There are many variations of this design—for instance, the ports in the cylinder walls as shown in Fig. 4 may in fact be air inlet ports, whilst the valves in the head become exhaust valves.

Both four-stroke and two-stroke single-acting designs employ open-ended pistons with the little end of the connecting rod secured to a gudgeon pin in the piston itself. No piston rod, guide bars or crosshead is employed and the type of piston used is known as the "trunk" type.

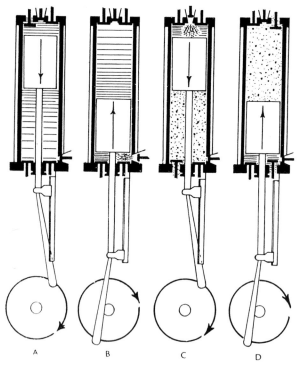

A   B   C   D

Fig. 5. Sequence of operations. Four-stroke double-acting engine.

FOUR-STROKE DOUBLE-ACTING (*See Fig.* 5)

In double-acting engines a considerably higher power output can be obtained without increasing the size of the cylinder bores or greatly increasing the overall dimensions of the engine. Although the number of power strokes in a two-stroke single-acting engine is twice that of a four-stroke s.a. engine, the power developed from a particular cylinder diameter is by no means doubled. This is due to the fact that, unlike the four-stroke engine, the working stroke of the two-cycle unit is not wholly effective because the inclusion of ports in the side of the cylinder controls and limits the source of power. In many cases the mean effective pressures of two-cycle engines are considerably lower than those of four-cycle motors of the same rated power. Designers have, therefore, turned to the *double acting* four-stroke design, and in this pattern a cylinder head is fitted at the top and bottom of the cylinder, as in the case of a steam engine. The provision of one or more injectors at the base of the cylinder results in two working strokes every two revolutions. The piston is not of the trunk pattern and in consequence a piston rod with a gland in the lower cylinder head is employed, whilst a crosshead and guide bars are also used.

Following the sequence shown in Fig. 5 we find that the piston is at the top of the cylinder and commencing to move downwards as the crankshaft turns (A). The upper inlet valve is open and clean air is being drawn into the cylinder whilst at the same time, below the piston, air is being compressed as both lower valves are closed. On the piston reaching the bottom of its stroke injection takes place beneath it and it rises on the first power stroke—at the same time compressing the air above it, the top inlet valve being closed (B).

Injection now takes place *above* the piston and it descends on the second power stroke (C) exhausting the burnt gases beneath it through the open lower exhaust valve. To complete the cycle the piston rises again drawing air through the lower inlet valve and exhausting the upper burnt gases past the now open exhaust valve (D). On reaching t.d.c. the downward stroke (A) will be recommenced.

This cycle of operations should be compared with the single-acting four-stroke shown in Fig. 3 and it will be observed that there is a working stroke for every revolution of the crank. The pistons of these engines are invariably hollow for cooling purposes, the cooling medium, either oil or water, is usually delivered by means of telescopic pipes.

TWO-STROKE DOUBLE-ACTING (*See Fig. 6 overleaf*)

These engines have two power strokes per revolution of the crank and thus each stroke of the piston is a working stroke. In this respect they are of course, contemporary with the steam engine and like most double-acting motors are fitted with a piston-rod and crosshead mounted on slide bars.

The two-stroke double-acting engine has two sets of ports midway down the cylinder. On one side is a single row of scavenging air ports

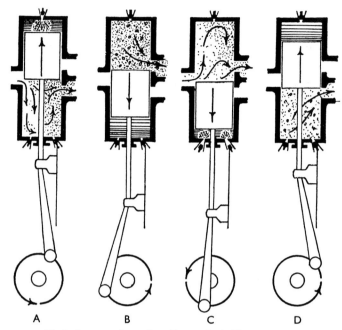

Fig. 6. Sequence of operations. Two-stroke double-acting engine.

and on the alternate side a double row of exhaust ports. The ports are arranged so that the exhaust openings are uncovered by the piston before the inlet ports.

Commencing just before t.d.c. we find the air compressed and the fuel being injected *above* the piston (A). Combustion takes place, the piston is driven downwards whilst underneath air is being compressed and the top exhaust ports are being uncovered (B). Later, the piston uncovers the scavenging ports, air from which blows out the burnt gases and recharges the cylinder, whilst towards b.d.c. the lower fuel injectors function and cause combustion to take place *below* the piston (C).

Next, the piston is forced upwards by the expanding gases beneath until the lower exhaust ports are uncovered and the scavenge ports cut off, causing compression on top of the piston to recommence the cycle of operations (D).

MULTI-CYLINDER-BANK ENGINES

In order to secure considerable increases in power without increasing the length of the engine various methods are adopted by designers. The most common of these is the vertical "Vee" bank arrangement (Fig. 30) and in the petrol-engine field most of us are familiar with the Ford "V8" motor which contains two banks of four cylinders each. This arrangement is particularly popular with engines for diesel-electric locomotive use in the higher horse-power ranges.

With the opposed-pistons type of engine, see pages 18-19, instead of the "flat" form (vertical or horizontal) that these usually take, more unorthodox grouping of the cylinders may be found. The Napier "Deltic" eighteen-cylinder traction engine is a typical example. The "Deltic" (Fig. 32) was originally developed for marine craft propulsion and there is also a nine-cylinder version of the design.

These are some of the various cylinder arrangements which can be encountered in rail traction engines but the more general vertical or horizontal in-line engines will be dealt with in detail later in this book.

FIRING ORDER

It will be appreciated that so far we have been dealing with single cylinders when describing cycles of operation, but normally 4, 5, 6, or 8 cylinders appear in in-line designs, whilst multiples of these numbers are used in multi-bank designs.

We must imagine the cycles of events previously described happening several hundreds of times a minute in each cylinder of an engine and arranged so that the power strokes occur one at a time in planned succession as the crankshaft revolves. The result is a very even and strong turning effort on the crankshaft. The sequence of power strokes is known as the "Firing Order" and in the popular four-stroke single acting six-cylinder designs is usually 1-5-3-6-2-4 reading from the front of the engine. In an eight-cylinder example, the Rolls-Royce horizontal engine illustrated on page 64, the firing sequence is 1-6-2-5-8-3-7-4.

OPPOSED-PISTONS TWO-STROKE (*See Fig. 7 overleaf*)

These engines have two individual pistons fitted in the same cylinder and the fuel injector or injectors are mounted at the side where the two pistons come almost together. The pistons operate as one, the second, in small engines, being connected to a second crankshaft which itself is connected through a train of gears to the main crankshaft. In the case of the "Deltic" engine a train of gears at the driving end of the unit connects the three crankshafts to a main output shaft located in the centre of the triangle. Two rows of ports are provided in the o.p. design, one being for air admission and the other for the escape of exhaust gases. The single-cylinder engine, as will be seen, fires once every revolution.

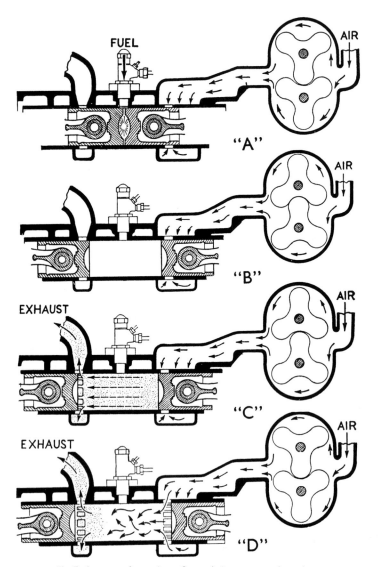

FUEL

AIR

"A"

AIR

"B"

EXHAUST

AIR

"C"

EXHAUST

AIR

"D"

Fig. 7. Sequence of operations. Opposed-pistons two-stroke engine.

On the compression stroke both pistons move inwards simultaneously and the air between them is compressed until, when the pistons have almost met, fuel injection takes place (A) and they are forced apart by the pressure of the expanding gases (B). When the left-hand piston reaches the end of the stroke it uncovers the exhaust ports and allows the exhaust gases to escape from the cylinder (C). Almost immediately after this the other piston uncovers the induction ports and clean air under pressure sweeps into the cylinder filling the space between the pistons with fresh air (D).

The end of the engine connected to the transmission units or electric generator is known as the "driving end," whilst the opposite end of the unit is called the "free end." In many installations the "free end" of an engine is employed to drive auxiliaries such as radiator-fans or dynamos, which absorb some of the diesel's power. However, the main power output is always absorbed at the "driving end." Engines may rotate in "clockwise" or "anti-clockwise" direction looking at the unit from the "free end." Rail traction diesels are generally made non-reversing owing to the limits imposed by the loading gauge, although it is common practice for marine diesels of large size to be of the reversible type due to sufficient space being available for the additional equipment necessary.

PRESSURE-CHARGING

We have already mentioned that low pressure "scavenge" air may be used on some engines and high pressure air (full supercharging) on others. Engines which are not supercharged (or have only a low pressure scavenge system around 2 lbs. per square inch) are usually referred to as "normally aspirated"—the density of air in the cylinders of such engines at the commencement of the compression stroke is about the same as that of the surrounding air and this determines the amount of fuel which can be burnt efficiently and therefore the engine's power output.

Now, if the density of air can be increased by supplying it under pressure to the intake, the weight of air in the cylinders is increased, more fuel can be effectively burnt and the engine power output improved. The air is supplied to the intake by means of a compressor unit or "charger" which may be mechanically driven from the engine, driven by a separate electric motor or by a free-running gas turbine using the engine exhaust gases. The latter method is the more efficient as it enables normally lost heat energy to be recovered—or a portion of it. The combined gas turbine and rotary compressor is termed the "turbo-blower", "turbo-charger" or "pressure-charger".

Essentially, the turbo-charger consists of a single-stage gas turbine connected to a single-stage centrifugal blower mounted on a common shaft.

Fig. 8. English Electric 12 cylinder CSVT engine illustrating pressure-chargers and charge-air coolers.

Exhaust gases from the engine are led into the turbine casing through a series of fixed nozzle blades, then directed to the blades on the turbine wheel and from there to atmosphere via the exhaust discharge system. The rotating turbine wheel drives the air impeller which draws in air, compresses it and discharges it to the engine's inlet manifold. The turbo-charger operates at speeds up to 30,000 r.p.m.

Charge-air pressures for four-stroke diesels were until quite recently as low as 5-6 lbs. per sq. inch and resulted in increases in power of up to 50 per cent over normally-aspirated engines of the same design. Today, however, charge-air pressures of 12-18 lbs. per sq. inch and increases in power of 100 per cent are not uncommon.

Usually such figures as above are produced by engines which employ charge-air cooling. During compression of the air in the blower the air temperature rises and in low-pressure systems the air discharged from the blower is about 80 degrees Fahrenheit above that of the surrounding atmosphere. As the air temperature increases, its *density* falls, in this case about 10 per cent, which does not matter a great deal. However, with higher charging pressures the temperature increases considerably and the density drop can be as much as 20 per cent (remember the object is to *increase* density). To counteract this it is usual to lead the air from the charger outlet to an air-cooler prior to delivering it into the intake manifold. The coolers are usually simple tubular types using water as the cooling medium. Apart from the increase in air density following reduction in temperature, designers do not like to employ high-temperature charge-air as this reduces the cooling effect on the piston top, cylinder walls and exhaust valves.

The majority of turbo-chargers are fitted with air intake filters which act also as air silencers and contain wire wool in a wire mesh container —the filter material being usually covered with a film of oil which traps the foreign matter in the induction air.

ENGINE SPEEDS

Compression-ignition oil engines for use with railway traction generally fall into two categories as far as maximum speed is concerned. Medium speed units which operate at aproximately 350 to 1,500 revolutions per minute, are generally employed for locomotive installations, whilst high speed units with governed speeds in excess of 1,500 r.p.m. are invariably found in railcars and multiple-unit trains. We shall illustrate these two particular classes, through the medium of well known examples, in Chapters Four and Five.

CHAPTER THREE

THE DIESEL ENGINE
FUEL INJECTION

IN EVERY PIECE of machinery there is a "brain" and, as in the human body, the whole is co-ordinated from this centre. Should this vital component suffer in any way from maladjustment or wear and tear, the machine will cease to be efficient. In a steam locomotive the valve gear is the nerve centre and petrol engines have their carburettors and ignition systems.

The nerve centre of the diesel engine is the fuel injection system, comprising a fuel injection pump and injectors together with the necessary feed pumps, filters, supply tanks and pipe lines. This equipment is provided in order to introduce into the cylinder of the engine an accurately metered amount of fuel at exactly the right moment. The fuel oil must be finely atomised and distributed throughout the combustion chamber in such a manner that each particle makes contact with oxygen.

FUEL SYSTEM

A typical layout of fuel injection components is shown in Fig. 9 and it can be seen that the fuel feed pump (3) draws diesel oil from the main storage tank (1) via the primary filter (2) which has a coarse element, and thence delivers it to the injection pump gallery or suction chamber by way of the secondary filter (8). This secondary filter is equipped with a pressure relief valve enabling surplus oil to be returned to the storage tank. The primary filter is usually fitted with a coarse element whilst the other has a renewable element of paper. *It is of vital importance that all fuel filters receive regular cleaning.*

Whilst the layout illustrated is a typical one, it should be mentioned that many installations have more than two filters. For details of fuel filter construction see page 45.

FUEL FEED PUMP (*See Fig.* 10 *overleaf*)

The fuel feed pump or lift pump, the function of which is to draw fuel from the storage tank and deliver it to the injection pump, may consist of a small diaphragm- or plunger-type unit bolted directly to the multi-barrel injection pump although in the case of larger engines an electric motor-driven pump of much larger dimensions is employed.

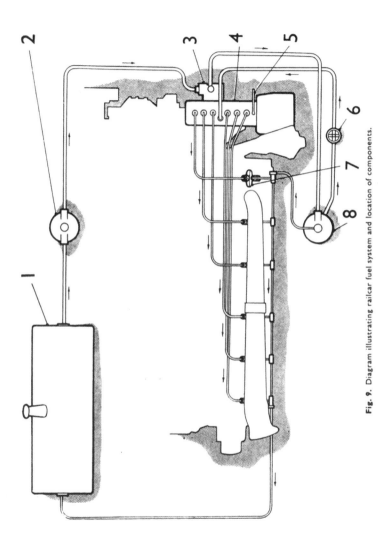

Fig. 9. Diagram illustrating railcar fuel system and location of components.

When the cam (12) is in the position of minimum lift as shown in diagram D, the spring (13) forces plunger (7) down so that the fuel is sucked up from the tank through inlet (2) and into inner chamber (14). During the same movement the opposite side of the plunger forces the fuel from the outer chamber (15) through connecting channel (16) into fuel outlet (3).

As the cam turns and lifts the plunger, the inlet valve (6) is closed and the fuel forced past outlet valve (5) through connecting channel (16) into the outer chamber (15), as shown in diagram E. It will be seen that the upward stroke of the plunger (7) effected by the cam (12) is not the pumping stroke. As the cam returns to the bottom position fuel is delivered due to the spring-operated return stroke of the plunger which displaces fuel from chamber (14) into outlet (3), the valve (5) now being closed.

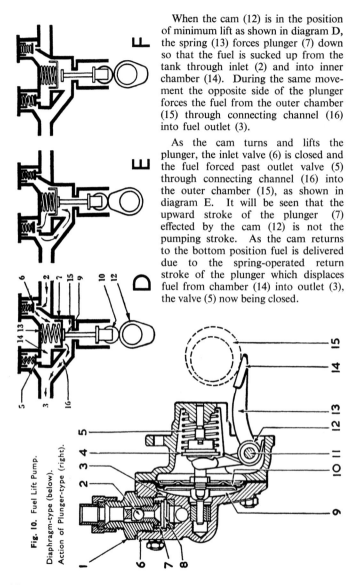

Fig. 10. Fuel Lift Pump.
Diaphragm-type (below).
Action of Plunger-type (right).

FUEL INJECTION

The diaphragm type fuel feed pump shown in Fig. 10 (lower illustration) is also shown attached to a C.A.V. hydraulically governed injection pump in Fig. 20. The key to Fig. 10 is given below:—

1. Union, outlet to filter

2. Ball valve

3. Fuel passage to diaphragm chamber

4. Spring plate

5. Diaphragm spindle spring

6. Housing

7. Disc valve spring

8. Disc valve

9. Cavity

10. Diaphragm pack and support plates

11. Housing

12. Bellcrank lever spring

13. Bellcrank lever

14. Thrust pad

15. Camshaft eccentric

INJECTION PUMP

The injection pump having been fed with fuel oil from the feed pump must now deliver the fuel to the injectors and it has the task of metering the fuel and delivering it at the right time. A high degree of atomisation must be provided and further, the fuel must when entering the cylinder penetrate the charge of compressed air. Consequently injection pressures are high ranging from 1,000 lbs. per square inch to 10,000 lbs. p.s.i. To perform these functions at such high pressures the pumps must be extremely accurately built and in fact pump manufacturers often work to measurements of one-20,000th part of an inch.

For high-speed engines, pumps are invariably constructed in multi-element form, a separate pump for each cylinder being built into one complete assembly. For the larger, locomotive type engines it is normal for a separate pump to be mounted at each cylinder although the principle of operation remains the same. The cams which operate the pumps revolve at half engine crankshaft speed in four-stroke designs and at full engine speed in the case of two-stroke motors.

A complete injection pump of C.A.V. manufacture is illustrated by Fig. 11 (overleaf). It is fitted with a mechanical two-speed governor.

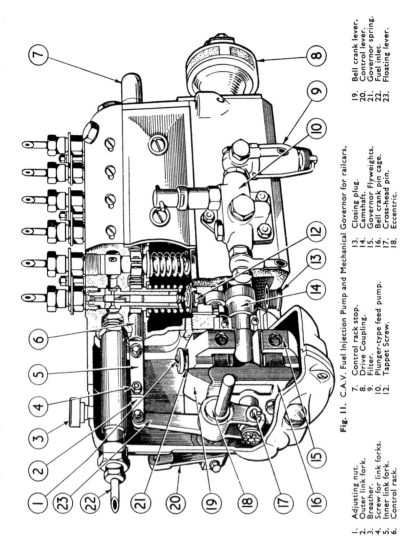

Fig. 11. C.A.V. Fuel Injection Pump and Mechanical Governor for railcars.

1. Adjusting nut.
2. Outer link fork.
3. Breather.
4. Screw for link forks.
5. Inner link fork.
6. Control rack.

7. Control rack stop.
8. Drive Coupling.
9. Filter.
10. Plunger-type feed pump.
12. Tappet Screw.

13. Closing plug.
14. Camshaft.
15. Governor Flyweights.
16. Bell crank pin cage.
17. Cross-head pin.
18. Eccentric.

19. Bell crank lever.
20. Control lever.
21. Governor spring.
22. Fuel inlet.
23. Floating lever.

Fuel enters through the pipe and union shown at item (22) in Fig. 11 from where it is supplied to the gallery through which each of the plungers obtains its supply. A vent cock is provided for releasing air from the system as necessary. Lubrication is arranged by splash feed from the sump and a certain amount of fuel oil which leaks back into the lubricant is used to keep the pump oil level topped up and, although the original lubricating oil is thinned by this process, experience has proved that the pump will operate quite satisfactorily.

The control rack (6) which controls the amount of fuel delivered, may be observed protruding from the body of the pump within its housing at (7) in Fig. 11. A small pipe near the base of the unit is employed to conduct back to the main tank any surplus fuel oil from the sump caused through the "leaking back" previously mentioned.

Medium speed locomotive engines used for main line and shunting applications have separate pump units for each cylinder and one of these may be seen in Fig. 12—the internal construction is almost identical with that about to be described. Again a pump rack is provided for control but this is connected to a long control shaft which is laid along the top of each bank of cylinders as shown in Fig. 16. Although just two pump units appear in the illustration there may be as many as 16 in two rows of eight. Control is arranged from a centrifugal type governor, the balance weights of which operate a valve, allowing lubricating oil to flow into or out of a servo cylinder, the piston of which operates the fuel racks. More details of this control and governing generally are given elsewhere in this book.

There are several other types of fuel-injection pumps but typical examples of the C.A.V. range are illustrated, although it should not be forgotten that equipment of Bryce and Simms manufacture is frequently encountered in rail traction service. The pump illustrated in Fig. 11 is fitted with a plunger-type fuel lift the action of which is illustrated on page 24.

In the case of railcar engine fuel injection pumps a shut-down solenoid is mounted on the casing of the two-speed governor. This electrically operated feature ensures, when it is energised, that the pump rack is pushed until the pump elements are in the position "f" in Fig. 14 and the engine is stopped. The solenoid is operated automatically in the event of low lubricating oil-pressure or water level in the cooling system.

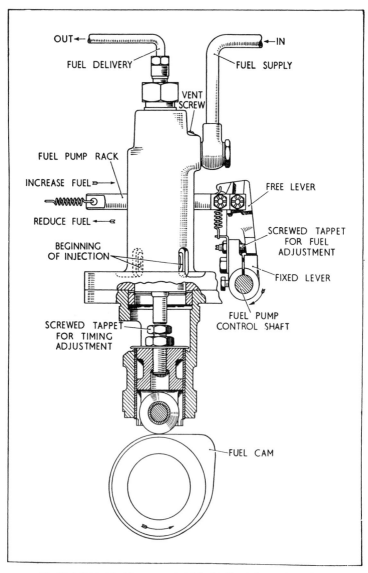

OUT ← FUEL DELIVERY IN → FUEL SUPPLY

VENT SCREW

FUEL PUMP RACK

INCREASE FUEL ▷

REDUCE FUEL ←

FREE LEVER

BEGINNING OF INJECTION

SCREWED TAPPET FOR FUEL ADJUSTMENT

FIXED LEVER

FUEL PUMP CONTROL SHAFT

SCREWED TAPPET FOR TIMING ADJUSTMENT

FUEL CAM

Fig. 12. Individual Fuel Pump as used with English Electric locomotive engines.

PUMP ELEMENTS   (*See Fig.* 13)

A single element is illustrated and consists primarily of a pump barrel (G) and a plunger (H) of hardened steel,   Fuel oil is taken from a common gallery and the stroke of the plunger (H) is constant but the *effective* pumping stroke can be varied by means of a control quadrant (O).

Rotation of the plungers to effect any required delivery position between "stop" and "full load" is carried out in the following manner.   The bottom end of the plunger (H) has a lug (J) and this engages in a slot of the control quadrant (K). At its uper flange the quadrant is equipped with teeth and these engage with similar teeth on the control rack (L). The rack runs the length of the pump and is in mesh with the quadrant of each pumping element.   Movement of the rack backwards and forwards rotates all the plungers and thus selects the position of the helices to accord with the fuel delivery rate desired.

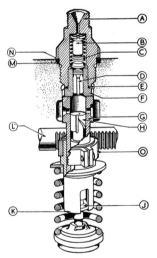

Fig. 13

A single Fuel Injection Pump Element.

A. Delivery valve holder.
B. Spring peg.
C. Delivery valve spring.
D. Delivery valve.
E. Washer.
F. Delivery valve seat.
G. Plunger barrel.
H. Plunger.
J. Plunger locating lug.
K. Control sleeve.
L. Control rod.
M. Rubber seal.
N. Washer.
O. Control quadrant.

Fig. 15 shows close-ups of the plunger and barrel, from which the operation can be easily followed.   The sloping portion of the plunger is known as the "helix" and when the plunger is at the bottom of its stroke (a), fuel oil can enter the barrel through the ports. As the plunger rises the top edge covers the ports (b). Fuel oil is now forced out through the delivery valve and so to the injector.   As the plunger rises, pumping is continued until the edge of the helix reaches the lower edge of the ports and allows the fuel to escape (c), releasing the pressure and bringing to an end actual *pumping* portion of the stroke.   The plunger now completes

29

its stroke without any further pumping and is subsequently returned to the bottom by action of the plunger spring.

The quantity of fuel oil pumped depends on the length of the pumping portion of the stroke between the points shown in Fig. 14 (b and c). This "effective" stroke is varied by rotating the plunger so as to bring a higher or lower portion of the helix into line with the ports and this action is well illustrated below, (c) full load, (d) half load and (e) idling respectively.

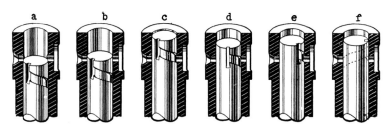

Fig. 14. Action of the Injection Pump Elements.
a. fuel admission; b. commencement of delivery; c. full load; d. half load; e. idling; f. stop.

Again, examining Fig. 14, it will be noticed that at its upper end the helix joins a vertical groove running down from the crown of the plunger. If this groove is in line with the port, the oil in the barrel is afforded a means of escape and thus no pumping stroke is possible. This is the "stop" position, during which no fuel is delivered and is illustrated by (f).

DELIVERY VALVE

It is necessary, in order to effect instantaneous release of pressure in the fuel lines after the plunger has completed its injection stroke, to provide a non-return delivery valve and one of these is situated at the outlet of each pumping element. The delivery valve is lifted from its seat when the pump delivery occurs and the oil passes through as in the right-hand illustration of Fig. 15. When delivery has

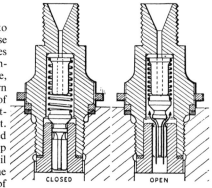

Fig. 15. Fuel Injection Pump Delivery Valve.

ended by the opening of the ports, the sudden collapse of pressure in the pump causes the valve to snap back sharply on to its seating under the influence of the coil spring and it remains closed as in the left-hand illustration until pressure is again built up for injection.

GOVERNING

The method of controlling the fuel rack (governing) varies with the particular application but may be:—

(*a*) By centrifugal means through a series of rotating weights controlling rack movement.

(*b*) Pneumatically, where a leather spring-loaded diaphragm is coupled to the rack and controlled by the vacuum in the engine air intake.

(*c*) Hydraulically, whereby oil pressure from a built-in pump controls the rack.

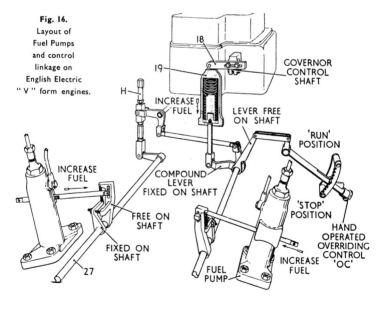

Fig. 16.
Layout of
Fuel Pumps
and control
linkage on
English Electric
" V " form engines.

18

19

GOVERNOR
CONTROL
SHAFT

H

INCREASE
FUEL

LEVER FREE
ON SHAFT

'RUN'
POSITION

INCREASE
FUEL

COMPOUND
LEVER
FIXED ON SHAFT

'STOP'
POSITION

FREE ON
SHAFT

HAND
OPERATED
OVERRIDING
CONTROL
'OC'

FIXED ON
SHAFT

INCREASE
FUEL

27

FUEL
PUMP

To illustrate typical governor systems, that of an English Electric "V" form engine and a B.U.T. horizontal railcar engine have been selected and are illustrated on pages 33 and 34 respectively. These two systems are examples of the "all-speed" and "two-speed" type of fuel injection pump governors and in these particular instances the former is applied to an engine which has a separate fuel pump for each cylinder and the latter a monobloc type fuel pump with governor complete as a single unit. The pneumatic type (all-speed) governor, (b) above, is also applied to railcar engines but not, generally speaking, in this country.

ENGLISH ELECTRIC GOVERNOR

Contained within the casing shown at the rear in Fig. 16 is a governor servo mechanism which operates the fuel pump control shafts (27) via the governor control-shaft lever (18). This rotary movement of the shafts (27) is converted into sliding movement at the racks of the individual fuel pumps determining the amount of fuel injected in the same manner as illustrated in Fig. 14 (page 30). In Fig. 17, which illustrates the governor unit, the weights (20) are rotated by the engine and the resultant centrifugal force is balanced by a spring (17). The port (21) is connected to the lubricating oil system which supplies oil under pressure to the governor unit. When the governor is in equilibrium, as shown in Fig. 17, the pilot valve (25) prevents any oil flow but if the load on the diesel increases, its speed drops and the weights (20) move inwards, the valve (25) is lowered, and lubricating oil flows to the servo cylinder raising the piston (9), which is connected to the fuel injection pump control shafts. The delivery from the injection pumps then increases and restores engine speed. The rising piston (9) rotates the levers (12) about their fulcrum (15), thus decreasing the compression of the spring valve (17) and the weights (20) move outwards. The position of equilibrium now corresponds to a slightly lower engine speed than before.

If the load on the engine decreases, the valve (25) rises and allows oil to escape from below the piston (9), the return spring (11) pushes the piston downwards and an equilibrium position will again be reached, this time at a slightly higher speed than before. The position of the shaft (7) determines the setting of the governor spring, and the servo mechanism of this governor cannot operate unless oil under pressure is available to move the piston (9).

In addition to the governor described, an emergency overspeed trip is fitted so that if, for any reason, the diesel engine exceeds its maximum speed, a trigger mechanism operates and cuts off the fuel supply to the injectors so stopping the engine. A manually-operated shut-down control is provided also and the lever (OC in Fig. 16) represents the type used on "V" form engines. It will be appreciated that there is also a control system which is directly operated by the driver in his cab and this is described and illustrated in a later chapter.

FUEL INJECTION

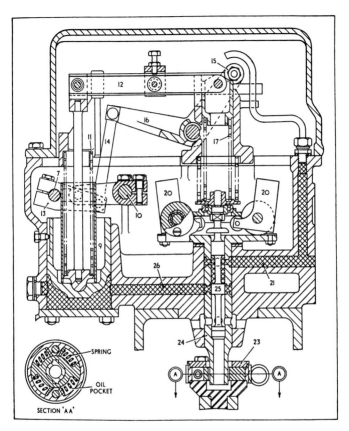

Fig. 17. English Electric governor servo mechanism.

TWO-SPEED GOVERNOR (*See Figs.* 11 *and* 18)

This is a mechanical governor of the idling and maximum speed type using the well-known principle of flyweights used on some reciprocating steam engines. The governor allows an idling engine speed when the throttle controller is closed, to enable the engine to run slowly without stalling, and a maximum speed which will not damage the engine. The

33

movement of the two flyweights (L) which are mounted on an extension of the injection pump camshaft (K) is restricted by sets of compression springs. One set restrains the weights until idling speed is reached and if the idling speed rises above normal the weights over-coming the springs move outwards and by means of the two bell-crank levers (M) the pump control rod (P) is moved towards the "stop" position. If the idling speed falls below that required the reverse action takes place.

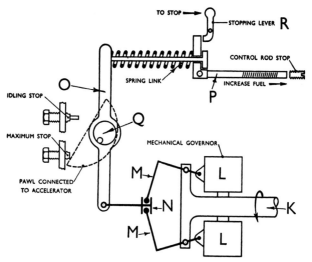

Fig. 18. Diagram to illustrate principle of C.A.V. Idling and Maximum Speed Mechanical Governor.

Between idling and maximum speeds the engine is under direct control of the throttle control lever, and this works independently of the control rod by means of the eccentric shaft (Q) through the fulcrum point of the floating lever (O). The governor weights during this period are restricted in their outward movement by the outer springs in the set and it is not until these are compressed that the governor again takes control. At this point the predetermined maximum is achieved and once the tension of the springs is overcome the weights travel outwards, withdrawing the control rod and holding the engine at maximum speed.

The forward position of the pump control rod (P) i.e. movement from the left to the right in Fig. 18, is limited by a maximum speed stop which is pre-set when the engine is factory tested. In addition there is an idling speed adjustable stop which is normally set to give 375-400 r.p.m. on railcar engines. An auxiliary idling damper-screw is fitted in the end of the governor casing and by contact with lever (O) damps out oscillations of the rod (P). The engine can be stopped by the operation of an electric solenoid which is mechanically connected to the stop lever (R) on the side of the governor housing and when operated moves the pump control rod (P) to the fuel cut-off position, thereby stopping the engine.

The two-speed governor described is fitted to the majority of railcar engines on British Railways. There are however, an increasing number of units where more positive control is obtained throughout the engine speed range (375-2,000 r.p.m.) and hydraulic "all speed" governors are used on these applications. Details of this type of C.A.V. governor are given overleaf, whilst on pages 40-41 a description of the latest type of injection pump appears.

ALL-SPEED GOVERNOR (see Fig. 19 overleaf)

The unit is enclosed in an aluminium casting designed to be attached directly to the injection pump in a similar manner to the two-speed governor shown on page 26. The diagram shows the hydraulic circuit employing a principle of hydraulic governing which achieves extreme accuracy and sensitivity of control. Use is made of the "inverted hydraulic amplifier" through which a small pressure change in one part of the system produces an opposite change of much greater magnitude in another part.

The rack (J) is attached to a drag link (K) pivoting at point (V) on the governor lever. At the top of this lever a swing link (L) is connected to the servo piston (G) which is spring-loaded on one side.

The gear-type pump (A) is driven from the camshaft receives its fuel supply from the injection pump gallery and delivers it to an amplifier piston (F). The amplifier piston has a metering hole allowing fuel to pass to the servo piston (G), forcing it against spring (H) and thus moving the rack (J) to an "increased delivery" position.

The amplifier valve stem (E) is in contact with the underside of the amplifier piston. The head of the valve is in contact with a spring-loaded plunger whose rating can be altered by movement of the operating lever (Y) within the limits of its maximum and minimum stops (X & Z).

Two relief valves (B & C) limit fuel pressure on each side of the servo piston. An idling valve (N) is loaded by spring (M) to the pump casing on one side and to the spring-loaded plunger (P) on its other side. Plunger (P) is in contact with the slow running screw (Q). Two bleed points (A1) are provided in the top of the governor casing to bleed either side of the servo piston.

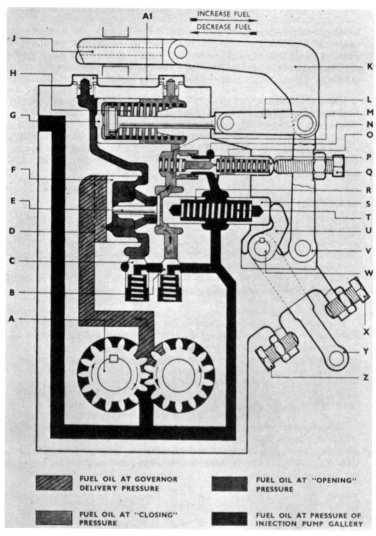

INCREASE FUEL
DECREASE FUEL

A1

J
H
G
F
E
D
C
B
A

K
L
M
N
O
P
Q
R
S
T
U
V
W
X
Y
Z

FUEL OIL AT GOVERNOR DELIVERY PRESSURE	FUEL OIL AT "OPENING" PRESSURE
FUEL OIL AT "CLOSING" PRESSURE	FUEL OIL AT PRESSURE OF INJECTION PUMP GALLERY

Fig. 19. Diagram of C.A.V. all-speed hydraulic governor.

On starting, the operating lever (Y) is moved to full travel thus loading the amplifier valve (E) and keeping it on its seat. The engine is now rotated by the starter motor and pump (A) begins to deliver fuel to the governor. The quantity of fuel flowing is small at this speed and the pressure-drop across the orifice of the amplifier piston is also very small; in consequence no appreciable end-thrust is developed and the amplifier valve stays closed whilst the fuel is trapped against the servo piston. As the "opening pressure" rises the servo piston (G) forces the rack open and fuel is delivered to the injectors until the engine fires.

As the engine gathers speed the increased fuel flow sets up a pressure difference across the amplifier piston which thrusts against and opens amplifier valve (E), thus admitting fuel to the "closing" side of the servo piston (G) which moves to operate the rack and reduce the fuel supply to the engine. If the operating lever is now closed the spring force holding the amplifier valve towards its seat is reduced. The amplifier valve (E) will now open further, allowing more fuel to flow past it, resulting in a higher closing pressure and a lower opening pressure. This will cause the servo piston (G) to move the rack to a position to give idling fuel and the idler valve (N) will now be in control, holding the r.p.m. steady.

On running up, the engine speed will respond to the operating lever movement causing a load to be put on the amplifier valve via the spring loaded plunger. This closes the valve partially or completely depending on the amount the throttle controller has been moved, and cuts-off or reduces the fuel passing to the spring side of the servo piston ("closing pressure"), causing a sharp rise of pressure on the "opening" side of the servo piston, and as a result the servo piston moves rapidly to the "open" position forcing the rack to an increased delivery position until the engine reaches the speed selected.

The pressure difference across the amplifier piston has increased at this point moving the amplifier valve off its seat and causing the "opening" pressure to fall and the "closing" pressure to rise. This permits the servo piston and rack to move towards the "decrease fuel" position. The servo piston is halted when the "closing" pressure has reached a quantity where the low pressure valve opens and bleeds back to the pump (and out of the circuit) the same quantity of fuel which is passed into the circuit by the pump.

If a load is applied to the engine the governor will endeavour to maintain the engine speed constant. If the r.p.m. tends to fall due to increased load the reduction in fuel-flow lowers the amplifier piston end-thrust allowing the amplifier valve to close slightly. This has the effect of reducing the "closing" pressure and increasing the "opening" pressure, so that the servo piston and rack move to an increased fuel delivery position to maintain the selected r.p.m.

If the load continues to increase, the servo piston and rack continues moving towards the increased delivery position until the maximum stop is reached and this represents the maximum power available from the engine.

Should the load be *decreased* the r.p.m. will try to rise causing the pressure difference across the amplifier piston also to rise. The amplifier valve will as a result move off its seat giving an increase in "closing" pressure and a decrease in "opening" pressure thus moving the servo piston and rack to a lower delivery position again maintaining selected r.p.m.

In order to reduce the effective permanent rate of the governor so that for any change of load or resistance at idling its effect on engine speed will be small, an idling valve is incorporated to sample the "closing" pressure. This valve functions as follows: an adjusting screw (Q) on the governor lever (V) is in contact with a spring-loaded plunger (P). Movement of the plunger will impart a movement to the idling valve. The valve is fluted so that as it moves to the right the bleed from the spring side of the servo piston is decreased and vice-versa.

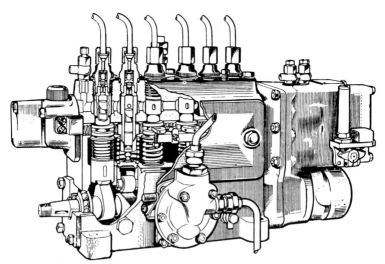

Fig. 20. C.A.V. "N" injection pump with "H" type hydraulic all-speed governor.

DISTRIBUTOR TYPE INJECTION PUMP

On some railcar engines readers may observe the C.A.V. "DPA" type distributor injection pump. In this design the fuel is pumped by a single element irrespective of the number of engine cylinders, the fuel being distributed to each injector by means of a rotary distributor. In the multi-cylinder in-line type pump (Fig. 20) the output of each element has

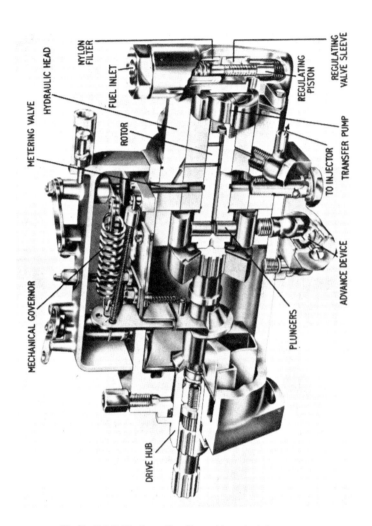

Fig. 21. C.A.V. Distributor Type Pump with mechanical governor.

to be adjusted separately and in correct relation to the others, whilst the distributor pump automatically ensures equal delivery to each injector and accurate phasing as the timing intervals between injection strokes are determined by exact spacing of distribution ports.

The D.P.A. pump is compact (compared with the in-line type) and forms an oil-tight unit lubricated by the fuel passing through it. Speed control is obtained in the normal way by means of either a mechanical flyweight or hydraulic type governor.

The central *rotating* steel member is known as the pumping and distributing rotor and is driven by splines from a drive shaft carried in the base of the pump housing. At its outer-end the rotor carries a vane type fuel-lift pump. The rotor is a close fit in a steel body (called the hydraulic head) and its pumping section has a transverse bore containing two opposed pump plungers. These plungers are operated through the medium of a stationary internal cam-ring located in the pump housing, via actuating rollers and shoes sliding in the rotor. The opposed plungers have no springs but are moved outwards by fuel pressure.

The distributing part of the rotor contains a central passage which connects the pumping space between the plungers with ports drilled radially in the rotor allowing for fuel inlet and delivery. One of these radial holes is the distributing port and as the rotor turns, it comes into line with each of the six outlet ports in the hydraulic head from whence the injectors are fed through normal high-pressure injector pipes. A similar number of inlet ports are spaced round the rotor and come into line successively with a single port in the head—this being the inlet or "metering port" which admits fuel under control of the governor.

Fuel entering the pump passes through a gauze filter to the inlet side of the lift pump. At this stage the fuel pressure is raised to an intermediate level controlled by a piston-type regulating valve and fuel at this pressure then passes through a passage in the hydraulic head to a chamber which houses the "metering valve". The metering valve is operated by the engine throttle and regulates the flow of fuel through the metering port into the pumping section of the rotor.

Pumping and distribution of the metered fuel oil is clearly illustrated in Fig. 22. The left-hand diagram shows the inlet or charging stroke and the right-hand diagram the distribution and injection. As the rotor turns, a charging port in the rotor is aligned with the inlet port in the hydraulic head and fuel oil at metered pressure flows into the central passage in the rotor and forces the plungers apart.

The amount of plunger movement is determined by the amount of fuel which can flow into the element while the ports are aligned—see left-hand diagram. The inlet port closes as rotation continues and as the single distributor port in the rotor comes into alignment with one of the distributor ports in the hydraulic head, the actuating rollers contact the cam-ring lobes and the plungers are forced inwards as shown in the right-hand diagram. High pressure is thus generated and fuel passes to the injector.

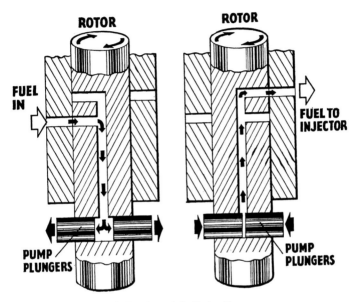

Fig. 22. Pumping and distribution diagram.
Left—Inlet stroke;   Right—Injection stroke.

INJECTORS

We have already seen how the fuel injection pump delivers the exact quantity of fuel oil at the correct time in proportion to the work to be done by the engine. To ensure that the fuel is delivered right into the combustion space, correctly distributed and finely atomised, an injector is necessary. A failure on the part of this precision-built component will result in faulty running of the engine and that gravest of crimes—a dirty exhaust. Several types of injectors are employed for rail traction diesel engines and they usually incorporate a spring-loaded needle valve which lifts under pressure of fuel.

41

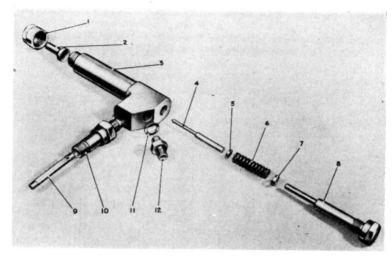

Fig. 23. Components of Leyland injector.

1. Locknut.
2. Nozzle.
3. Injector body.
4. Needle Valve.
5. Needle Valve Lift Distance Washer.
6. Valve Spring.
7. Discharge Pressure Adjusting Washer.
8. End Plug.
9. Edgewise Filter.
10. Inlet Adaptor.
11. Copper Washer.
12. Leak-off Adaptor.

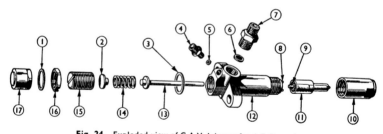

Fig. 24. Exploded view of C.A.V. Injector for A.E.C. engines.

1. Copper Washer.
2. Spring Plate.
3. Copper Washer.
4. Dribble Pipe Connection.
5. Copper Washer.
6. Disc Filter.
7. Inlet Connection.
8. Dowels
9. Nozzle Valve.
10. Nozzle Cap Nut.
11. Nozzle Body.
12. Injector Body.
13. Nozzle Valve Rod.
14. Spring
15. Spring Cap.
16. Locknut.
17. End Cap.

42

A typical example is illustrated in Fig. 23 and it will be seen that fuel from the injection pump enters the inlet adaptor (10) within which is a filter (9). The fuel oil is now fed through a drilled passage in the body (3) to the nozzle itself (2). When the required pressure is attained the needle valve (4) snaps open and allows fuel to be sprayed into the combustion chamber by means of four equally spaced holes in the tip of the nozzle. Although needle valves are a very fine fit in the injector body, a small quantity of fuel seeps past the valve stem and this is taken by way of a drilled passage to a gallery pipe leading to the supply tank. The injector shown in Fig. 23 is of the Leyland type, whilst in Fig. 24 an injector of C.A.V. design is shown and this particular example also has four spray holes, each of which is 0.35 mms. in diameter.

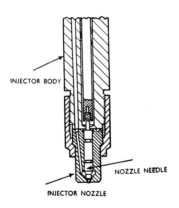

INJECTOR BODY

NOZZLE NEEDLE

INJECTOR NOZZLE

Fig. 25. Pintle type fuel injector nozzle.

Not all injectors are of the multi-hole type, some of them being designed with a single orifice of the self-cleaning (or "pintle") type which is generally found in ante-chamber high speed engines (see Fig. 25). Injectors for locomotive engines of medium speed follow the same principles but are of increased size. High speed engine injectors are fitted into a copper sheath in the cylinder head which ensures that a gas tight joint is made when the holding down nuts are tightened. It is of the utmost importance that the injector nozzle does not leak in service. This defect, if it occurs, is known generally as "dribble," takes place immediately after the needle valve closes, and can lead to the formation of carbon deposits.

Needle valve and nozzle seat must provide a perfect seal and with this in view the needle angle is more obtuse than the angle of the seat with which it mates, ensuring an almost knife edge contact. To ensure correct operation injectors require testing and resetting at stipulated periods during the life of an engine.

Injectors are tested and re-set with equipment of the hand-operated type. Briefly, the injector, after being inserted and coupled to the hand pump delivery pipe, is subjected to strokes of the pump which force the needle valve to "lift". The pressure at which the valve is lifting is indicated by means of a gauge. Although injector settings vary, in the case of the injector seen in Fig. 23 the correct setting is 140–145 atmospheres (i.e. 2,057–2,130 lbs. per square inch) whilst that in Fig. 24 is set to 175 atmospheres (2,540 lbs. per square inch).

INJECTION TIMING   (*See Fig.* 26)

The injection and valve timing of a typical six cylinder railcar engine of the high speed type is shown in the illustration, and injection commences at 26 degrees before t.d.c. and finishes at t.d.c. (this diagram should of course be read in a clockwise direction). The two rings shown in this illustration indicate the movement of the inlet valves (outer ring) and exhaust valves (inner ring). As this particular example is a single-acting four-stroke, the sequence is as follows: the inlet valve opens at 10 degrees before t.d.c. and remains open until 50 degrees after b.d.c., compression takes place and injection commences, as already mentioned,

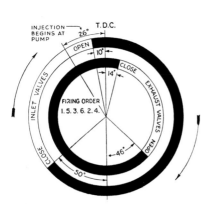

26 degrees before t.d.c. With valves closed the piston desends on the power stroke and the exhaust valve opens 46 degrees before b.d.c., remaining open throughout the scavenging stroke until it closes at 14 degrees after t.d.c. It is therefore clear that both inlet and exhaust valves are open at the same time during 24 degrees of movement, 10 degrees of which are before and 14 degrees after top dead centre, when the inlet is just opening and the exhaust closing.

Fig. 26. Valve timing diagram for Leyland railcar engine.

FUEL FILTERS

Filters of the cloth and paper element types are generally in use today and located in the fuel supply system as outlined in Fig. 9. They are both of the cross-flow type and the former consists of a bowl housing a close-weave fabric element pleated to a cylindrical form over a wire cage and secured by cotton twine. The assembly is generally the same for both types.

The filter illustrated has the fuel inlet (9) and outlet (4) carried in the top cover (8) which, in addition, has an air vent (5) and a bracket for the support of the assembly. The bowl (10) is of pressed steel and forms an oil-tight container for the element (2). A drain plug (1) is provided at the bottom of the bowl.

The paper element, contained in a thin metal canister, is wound round a circular core in such a manner as to provide a large filter area. A small rubber sealing ring (3) is fitted to the top of the element and a large one (lower 3) fitted on the centre spindle (12) in the bowl, seals the bottom of the element. The paper elements are not cleanable, nor can their condition be judged by external appearance. The unit is a very efficient filter but the element must be periodically replaced.

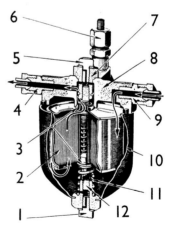

Fig. 27.

C.A.V. Paper element type fuel-oil filter in part-section.

 1. Drain Plug.
 2. Paper Element.
 3. Oil Seals.
 4. Outlet.
 5. Air Vent Plug.
 6. Air Release Valve Connection.
 7. Cap Nut.
 8. Cover.
 9. Inlet.
10. Bowl.
11. Pressure Spring.
12. Centre Stud.

CHAPTER FOUR

THE DIESEL ENGINE

MEDIUM SPEED ENGINES

HAVING examined the principles of combustion and fuel injection it is opportune to study complete engines and two modern units have been selected to illustrate medium speed units. To represent shunting locomotive installations the English Electric 6KT engine has been chosen, whilst the Paxman 16YHX, Napier Deltic and Sulzer LVA engines have been used to illustrate high horsepower units.

SHUNTING LOCOMOTIVE ENGINE.

This is a four-stroke single acting engine with six cylinders in line and this type is often coupled to an electric generator (see Chapter 9). The cylinder block and crankcase is in one piece this being known as monobloc construction. The main body of the engine is this casting made from alloy cast-iron and provided with large inspection doors to enable the main bearings and connecting rod big-end bearings to be removed. Other openings are provided to facilitate cleaning of the cylinder water jackets. Each cylinder has a bore of 10 inches accommodating a piston with a stroke of 12 inches.

The crankshaft, a steel forging made from high grade carbon steel, is toughened and hardened by heat treatment. At the driving end of the crankshaft is a flange to which a solid flywheel and the electric generator armature are coupled. The flywheel is a disc of alloy cast-iron and is recessed on its rim to enable the crankshaft to be barred round by hand. The position of the pistons and the timing of fuel injection and valve operation are indicated by a pointer on the crankcase and a graduated scale marked on the rim of this flywheel. The crankshaft is carried in main bearings consisting of steel shells lined with white metal. The bearing at the flywheel end has a greater length than the other main bearings, due to the extra load imposed upon it by the weight of the main generator armature.

The connecting rods for this engine are heat-treated carbon steel drop forgings and the small-end is bushed with phosphor bronze bearings

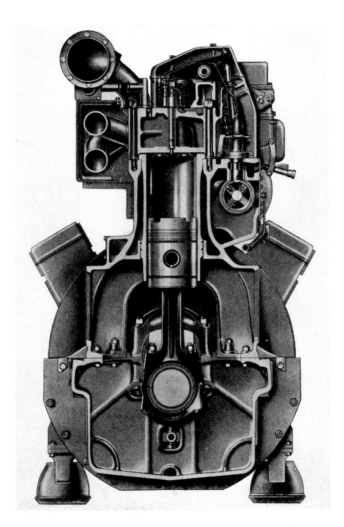

Fig. 28. Cross section of English Electric 6 SRKT engine.
(This is a supercharged version of the 6 KT.)

47

pressure lubricated by oil passed via the big-ends. The big-end bearings are white metal lined detachable steel shells.

Although the cylinders are contained in one casting, each has a separate cylinder head and the combustion chamber roof, inlet and exhaust port walls, together with the fuel injector locating sheath, are cooled with water passed from the crankcase by external pipes. Each separate cylinder-liner of alloy cast-iron is of the "wet" type, i.e., the outside of the liner is in direct contact with the cooling water. The valves are of the poppet type, an inlet and exhaust valve being fitted to each individual cylinder head, and each valve is spring-loaded by two coil springs. The inlet valves are made of nickel steel whilst the exhaust valves are manufactured from heat-resisting steel. These exhaust valves are contained in an easily removable cage, whilst the inlet valves are fitted directly into the cylinder heads. The engine's valve gear is lubricated directly from the engine pressure system.

Operating the valves is the camshaft which is mounted in three sections linked together by muff couplings which form the camshaft bearing journals. The drive is taken to the valves by means of cam followers and push rods.

The pistons employed are of the standard English Electric pattern manufactured from alloy cast-iron and each is fitted with three gas pressure rings and two oil control rings.

The lubricating oil and cooling water circulating pumps are driven from the front end of the crankshaft by means of helical gears. The water pump circulates the coolant through the engine and radiator, and after passing through the cylinder head cooling cavities, the water is taken to a jacket which surrounds the exhaust manifold. A thermostatically operated valve ensures that the engine is warmed up quickly after starting and that water is passed through the radiator at a rate which secures maintenance of an even engine temperature.

From the lubricating pump previously mentioned, oil which has been drawn from the engine sump through a non-return valve is delivered to the oil segment of the radiator from whence it passes into a large-area filter and passes on to the engine lubricating system. With this type of engine, oil must be circulated prior to starting and a hand-operated pump is provided for this purpose.

One fuel injection pump, driven from the camshaft, is provided for each cylinder and the engine is governed by a centrifugal governor with a hydraulic servo-gear operating the fuel pump control rack. The servo system is supplied with oil under pressure from the main lubrication system and is in itself an excellent safety device. The governor returns the fuel injection pumps to the "No Fuel" position if lubricating oil pressure fails and thus stops the engine.

This type of engine is started by temporarily converting the main generator into an electric motor powered by current from the storage batteries.

48

At 680 r.p.m. the 6KT engine develops 400 b.h.p. and its normal idling speed is 330 r.p.m. The unit has been specially designed for heavy duty where robust construction, low maintenance and maximum availability over prolonged periods are desired. The KT engine is one of the outstanding diesel motors developed in Britain for rail traction and variations of this design have been in continuous production for over twenty years.

There is also a supercharged version of this engine which is designated 6 SRKT (see Fig. 28) and the diesel-electric multiple-unit trains built by and operating in the Southern Region have this power unit, but in its four-cylinder form, mounted in each of the motor-coaches.

MAIN LINE LOCOMOTIVE ENGINE.

The Paxman "YH" series engines have been developed with the "Vee" bank cylinder arrangement and utilise two banks of cylinders pitched at

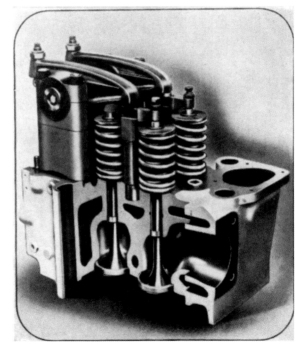

Fig. 29.
Part-
sectioned
view
of an
English
Electric
cylinder
head
(Vee form
engines).

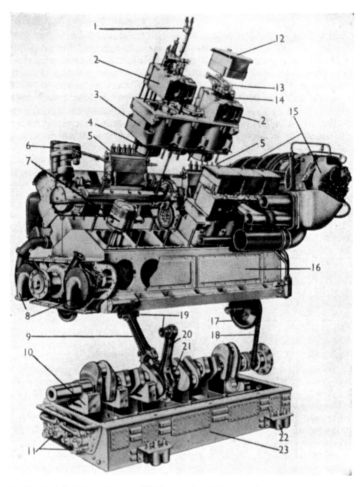

Fig. 30. Exploded View of Paxman "V" form engine. This particular example is a pressure-charged 12-cylinder unit of series YHX.

1. Fuel Injector; 2. Cylinder Head; 3. Cylinder Block; 4. Cylinder Liner; 5. Fuel Injection Pump; 6. Fuel Lift Pump; 7. Piston; 8. Water Circulating Pumps; 9. Connecting Rod (Plain Type); 10. Main Bearing; 11. Lub Oil Pumps; 12. Valve Cover; 13. Valve Rocker; 14. Valve Spring; 15. Exhaust Pressure Chargers; 16. Crankcase; 17. Camshaft Wheel; 18. Camshaft Roller Chain; 19. Connecting Rod Small End Bush; 20. Connecting Rod (Forked Type); 21. Crankshaft; 22. Engine Mounting; 23. Engine Underbed.

60 degrees. They are available in 12 and 16 cylinder formations. The 16 YHX engine is pressure-charged and develops 1,000 b.h.p. at 1,250 r.p.m. The cylinder diameter is 7.00 inches and the piston stroke 7.75 inches. At 1,000 r.p.m. one of these pistons travels 1,290 feet in one minute. In Paxman normally-aspirated engines a compression ratio of 17.25 to 1 is standard but the pressure-charged unit being described has a 14.25 to 1 ratio.

The engine is a four-stroke single-acting type and of lightweight alloy construction—an exploded view of the 12-cylinder version may be seen in Fig. 30. The crankcase carries the under-slung crankshaft and has housings to receive the cylinder liners. It is attached to the underbase which is fabricated from steel and forms a lubricating oil sump. The underbase provides a rigid means of mounting the four-point engine suspension system.

The crankshaft is a drop forging and is provided with balance weights, it is carried in ten main bearings which consist of steel housings, steel shells and copper lead linings. A double main bearing is located at the drive end where the camshaft gear wheel is mounted. A torsional vibration damper of the viscous type is fitted.

The connecting rods of the Paxman YHX engine are heat-treated carbon steel stampings and are accurately matched for both balance and weight. Attached to the lower end of the forked connecting rod is a block, housing the copper lead shell-type crankpin bearings. This block has a chromium-plated external surface on which the bearing of the mating (ordinary type) connecting rod rides. All big end bearings are of the replaceable shell pattern and are lead plated to assist their initial "running in" and prolong their working life.

Aluminium alloy pistons are fitted and carry three gas pressure and two oil control rings. The small end bushes are of silicon bronze and are used in conjunction with hollow bored gudgeon pins of the fully floating pattern retained by the usual circlips. Cylinder liners are formed from centrifugally cast high-grade iron. In the YHX unit a single cylinder head is fitted to each cylinder and is of aluminium alloy seated on the cylinder blocks with a spigot ring form of gasket. Each cylinder head carries two inlet and two exhaust valves, renewable aluminium bronze valve seats and a centrally located injector. The valve rocker gear of forged aluminium is carried on the upper face of the cylinder heads and is force lubricated from the main engine system. The camshaft is chain driven by means of a heavy duplex chain from the driving end of the crankshaft. The camshaft itself, a steel forging with hardened cams, is carried centrally between the "Vee" cylinder blocks in an independent cast-iron cambox. The cams run in an oil bath. Motion is conveyed to the valve rockers through the medium of roller-type cam followers and short pushrods.

Fig. 31. Cross Section of English Electric "V" form engine.
A. Piston; B. Cylinder; C. Injector; D. Fuel Pump; E. Valve Rocker; F. Crankshaft.

Immediately above the valve camshaft, and gear driven from it, is a jackshaft coupled to a further camshaft which operates the C.A.V. fuel injection pumps (clearly seen in Fig. 30). The fuel injectors are of the multi-hole needle type, spring loaded and are readily accessible. Cooling water is circulated by two centrifugal pumps, one for each bank, gear driven from the crankshaft. Lubricating oil is fed to the engine by means of engine-driven pumps and forced lubrication is employed throughout. The main pressure pump supplies lubricant via a full-flow element filter to the main gallery. A pressure relief valve controls the oil pressure at approximately 50 lbs. per square inch and incorporates a reducing valve to supply the camshaft and valve gear with oil at 10 lbs. pressure. The second lubricating oil pump is provided to pass oil at low pressure through the oil section of the radiator for cooling purposes.

Two centrifugal air compressors ("blowers"), driven by exhaust gas turbines are employed and mounted in line with the cylinder heads. The turbines are self-governing, their speed varying with engine speed, so that the amount of air delivered increases or decreases to correspond with the load on the engine. Pressure charged air is delivered to the induction manifold at 4–6 lbs. per square inch and by extending the period of maximum pressure in the cylinders, increases the engine output by 50 per cent.

Another example of a main line locomotive power-unit is the Deltic engine mentioned previously. This engine has given its name to the successful "Deltic" locomotive produced by English Electric and fitted with two Deltic diesels, the most powerful single-unit diesel-electric locomotive in the world at the time of writing.

In Fig. 32 is shown a cross section of this type of engine, which derives its name from an inverted Greek letter Δ and in Fig. 33 can be seen the main components of this interesting design. Although for traction purposes this engine has a maximum speed of 1,500 r.p.m. it can be classed as a medium speed unit for the purposes of this book. These engines are designed for quick replacement so that major repairs need not be carried out in position, a new feature for high-powered diesel locomotives although one accepted for high-speed railcar engines for a long time.

The way in which the Deltic engine is constructed may be seen from Fig. 33. There are three cylinder blocks, three crankcases, a phasing-gear casing and a scavenge blower. Many of these components are interchangeable, for example the three cylinder blocks (A) and two of the three crankcases (B) are similar—the lowermost one being odd as it is used as oil sump and engine mounting.

One of the main features of the "triangular" construction is the resulting compactness of the engine and the multitude of *small* cylinders give a low weight per horse power. Again, the rigidity of the Deltic form structure

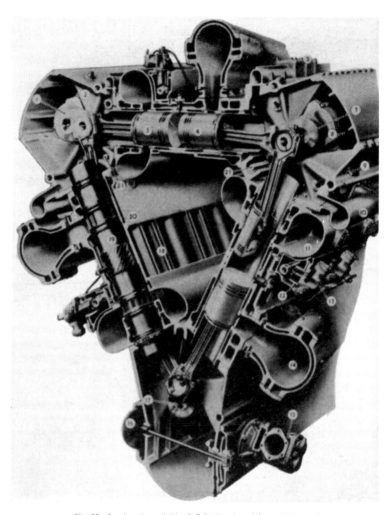

Fig. 32. Section through No. 5 Cylinder viewed from driving end.
Napier Deltic Opposed-Pistons Engine.

KEY: I. "BC" Crankshaft; 2. "BC" Crankcase; 3. Inlet piston; 4. Exhaust piston; 5. Crank-case Breather; 6. "AB" Crankcase; 7. "AB" Crankshaft; 8. Main Bearing Cap; 9. Crankcase Tie-Bolt; I0. Drain Oil Manifold; II. Air Inlet Gallery; I2. "A" Camshaft Casing; I3. Fuel Injection Pump; I4. Exhaust Manifold; I5. Water Pump; I6. Water Pump and Pressure Oil Pump Drive Gear; I7. "CA" Crankshaft; I8. Cylinder Block Tie-bolts; I9. Cylinder Liner; 20. "C" Cylinder Block; 21. Blower Flexible Drive Shafts.

enables the maximum use of light alloy castings with safety and reliability. The normal compression ratio is 19 to 1 and the cylinders fire at intervals equally spaced at 20° on the timing diagram—in fact the exhaust note of this engine is more like a turbine than a piston engine.

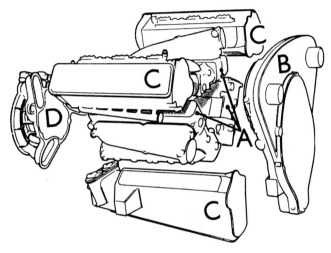

Fig. 33. Basic Components of Deltic engine.
A. Cylinder Blocks; B. Phasing Gear Casing; C. Crankcase; D. Blower.

SULZER LVA SERIES ENGINE

On the following page appears a section of the latest Sulzer engine for rail traction duties. Most Sulzer units for locomotives have been of the "in-line" type having all the cylinders in one or two straight rows. These "in-line" engines followed definite basic design principles—low speeds, simple but robust construction and a minimum number of cylinders and have been very successful.

The new "Vee"-form engine illustrated is a compact single-acting four stroke known as type LVA 24 produced in eight, twelve or sixteen cylinder versions all having a cylinder bore of 240 and piston stroke of 280 millimeters. In comparison with the "in-line" type of Series LDA 28 which develop their maximum horsepower at 750 r.p.m. the "V"-form engines have a maximum speed of 1,050 r.p.m. Exhaust gas turbocharging and charge-air cooling are employed. An interesting feature of this engine is that the crankshaft main bearing caps are hinged to the block for ease of

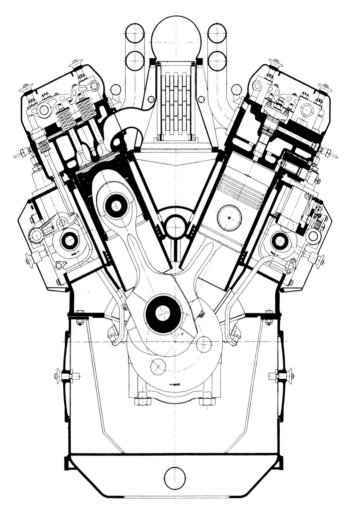

Fig. 34. Cross-section of Sulzer V-engine of Series LVA.

maintenance. The halves of both main and big-end bearings have serrated edges to ensure perfect alignment. No separate counterweights are fitted on the crankshaft, all the webs being of circular form but a torsional vibration damper is fitted at the free end of the shaft. The connecting rod big ends are located side-by-side thus permitting the use of rods of normal design (see Fig. 51 on page 78 for alternative fork and blade pattern). The big-ends are cut at an angle to allow removal of the connecting rods complete with pistons through the cylinder bores.

Pistons of the LVA 24 engine are oil-cooled and provided with four compression rings and two oil scraper rings, one above and one below the gudgeon pin. Twin inlet and exhaust valves are included in the design of the individual cylinder heads. A separate camshaft for each bank of cylinders is driven from the crankshaft but the camshaft is in separate sections (for each cylinder) bolted together by flanges. In the illustration the push-rod operated valves can be seen on the left cylinder head, whilst on the right head can be seen the centrally mounted injector, the fuel pump, and air-starting valve.

The drawing also clearly shows the serrations of the big-end bearing caps.

CHAPTER FIVE

THE DIESEL ENGINE

HIGH SPEED ENGINES

HIGH SPEED COMPRESSION-IGNITION oil engines are usually installed in railcars and multiple-unit trains, although they are sometimes employed in light shunting locomotives. In view of the fact that the horizontal type motor is installed in large numbers of British Railways railcars, the British United Traction 150 b.h.p. series of six cylinder units have been chosen as representative of this class of engine.

The B.U.T. "A" type engine developed by A.E.C. and the "L" type of Leyland origin are both four-stroke single acting designs and normally-aspirated. The vertical type of engine used in the ex-G.W.R. cars has not been promulgated on the national railway system, although B.U.T. have supplied this type of power unit in considerable numbers, installed in railcar chassis for the Irish Railways.

B.U.T. 150 B.H.P. ENGINE

The B.U.T.–A.E.C. engine is fitted with cylinders of 5.12 inches diameter and has a piston stroke of 5.59 inches. At 1,800 r.p.m. this engine develops 150 b.h.p. It is also produced as a 120 b.h.p. unit—having a cylinder bore of 4.72 inches and a common stroke. Both these designs are based on the same components, the smaller of the two units has been installed in two-axle type railcars for branch line operation, whilst the more powerful version is applied to bogie-type vehicles.

Fig. 35 shows the B.U.T.–A.E.C. 150 h.p. engine ready for installation in a multiple-unit train and fitted with a 20 inch diameter fluid coupling for use with the gearbox and allied transmission supplied to British Railways. A reciprocating type air-compressor is mounted on top of the engine as will be seen in the illustration, whilst the tachometer generator is gear driven from the fuel-pump drive.

The engine casing which is the main component, is divided vertically at the crankshaft centre line and comprises an integrally cast cylinder block and crankcase to which an engine casing extension and sump are bolted. This is a departure from the firm's vertical engine practice where the cylinder block is a separate casting to the crankcase upper-half. The casing is fitted with cylinder liners of renewable type which are formed from centrifugally cast cast-iron and detachable covers are provided to give access to the water spaces for cleaning purposes. Crankcase pressure is relieved through a breather on the engine casing extension.

Fig. 35. B.U.T.-A.E.C. horizontal railcar engine of the type fitted in large numbers to B.R. multiple-unit trains.

The mounting of the auxiliaries may be clearly seen in Fig. 35 above—the fuel injection pump (in the foreground) complete with fuel lift. To the right of the pump is the engine tachometer generator and immediately next to that are the crankshaft pulley (above) and the circulating water pump pulley (below). Vee-belts connect these two pulleys with the fan drive gearbox pulley at the extreme right of the picture and, framed in the triangle of these belts, is the lubricating oil cooler, which utilises engine cooling water to remove heat from the hot oil circulated through it.

Two detachable cylinder heads are employed, each covering three cylinders and the valve rocker-gear, valves and fuel injectors are carried in these heads. There is one inlet and one exhaust valve per cylinder.

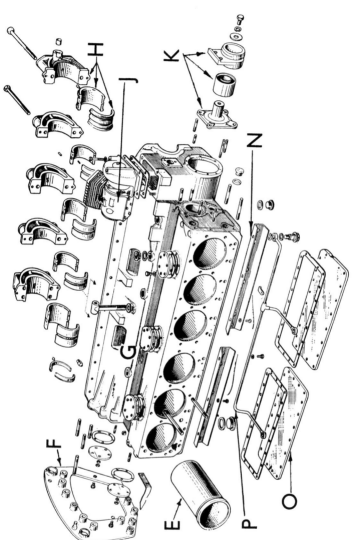

Fig. 36. Exploded view of monobloc—B.U.T.-A.E.C. 150 b.h.p. diesel.

E. Cylinder Liner.
F. Rear Support Bracket.

H. Main Bearings and Cap.
J. Air Compressor.

N. Push Rod Guide.
O. Push Rod Cover Plate.

The rocker-gear is operated by push-rods from a cam shaft and followers located in the engine casing. The cast-iron camshaft is carried in seven bushes and the cam faces are chill-hardened to give immunity from wear. A bevel gear attached to the camshaft at the front end provides a drive for the fuel injection pump.

The water pump which is mounted at the front of the engine, is driven by twin vee belts from the crankshaft pulley. The water pump inlet pipe from the radiator is located underneath the fan-drive tensioner pulley (Fig. 35). The outlet water pipe appears just above and to the left of the injection pump.

Each piston and connecting rod assembly (see Fig. 38) has a piston fitted with three gas pressure rings and two oil control rings. Lead-bronze bearings are provided for the big-ends and when worn, new bearings can be fitted and bored in a precision machine to the manufacturer's original dimensions. The A.E.C. crankshaft does not employ counterweights or a tortional vibration damper, although these are used in the Leyland engine. The particular example shown in Fig. 39 has hollow crank pins and main journals fitted with detachable end caps which when dismantled, allow the oil ways to be completely cleaned. On later A.E.C. engines such pads are only provided at the crank pins, the main journals being solid with small oil ways drilled in them.

The lubrication system of this engine employs two gear-type oil pumps mounted in tandem at the front of the engine below No. 1 main bearing, one of which is a pressure pump and the other used for scavenging purposes. Both pumps are driven from the front end of the crankshaft through helical gearing, the pressure-pump feeds lubricant to the main and big-end bearings as well as the idler gear bearings of the oil pump and timing gear drive. Pistons, gudgeon pins, tappets and all the camshaft bearings except the front one, are lubricated by splash whilst the valvegear and camshaft front bearing are fed with low pressure oil bled from the pump— the oil passing through the hollow rocker shafts and holes in the rockers themselves to the rocker pads. Surplus oil is drained through an internal oil grid into the well of the engine. The scavenge-pump then passes the oil through a filter and returns it to the sump.

The fuel-injection pump is mounted at right-angles to the crankshaft, this allows short injection delivery pipes to be used and these, as will be seen from the illustration, are neatly clipped together in groups of three. The governor is of the two-speed mechanical type. The fuel lift pump, by means of which the fuel is drawn from the main tank to the injection-pump is also clearly visible. The type of C.A.V. injector used with this engine is shown in Fig. 24 and is fitted with a disc-type final filtration element in the inlet-connection. The slight leakage of fuel oil

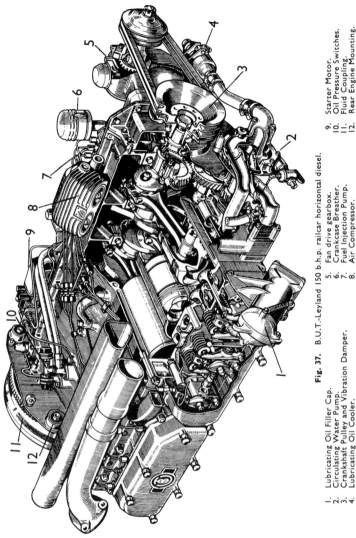

Fig. 37. B.U.T.-Leyland 150 b.h.p. railcar horizontal diesel.

1. Lubricating Oil Filler Cap.
2. Circulating Water Pump.
3. Crankshaft Pulley and Vibration Damper.
4. Lubricating Oil Cooler.

5. Fan drive gearbox.
6. Crankcase Breather.
7. Fuel Injection Pump.
8. Air Compressor.

9. Starter Motor.
10. Oil Pressure Switches.
11. Fluid Coupling.
12. Rear Engine Mounting.

which accumulates in the body of the injector is returned by means of "dribble" pipes to the supply system.

B.U.T.–Leyland engines are produced in standard 125 and 150 b.h.p. sizes, as are the B.U.T.–A.E.C. units. All four of these four-stroke horizontal designs have been employed in B.R. multiple-unit stock—

Fig. 38. B.U.T.-A.E.C. railcar engine piston and connecting rod P. Connecting Rod; Q. Combustion Chamber; R. Gas Pressure Rings; S. Oil Control Rings; T. Gudgeon Pin; U. Big End Bearing; V. Con. Rod Bolt.

Fig. 39. B.U.T.-A.E.C. railcar engine crankshaft. 1. Front oil-seal register; 2. Locknut locking washer; 3. Distance piece; 4. Thrust washer; 5. Thrust ring; 6. Grooves forming rear oil-seal; 7. Detachable end caps for hollow crankpins; 8. Timing drive gear; 9. Oil thrower; 10. Locknut.

Fig. 40. Part-sectioned close-up of a B.U.T.-Leyland diesel railcar engine.
1. Injector; 2. Injector Dribble Pipe; 3. Valve and Valve Seat; 4. Valve Rocker Shaft; 5. Valve Rocker Ball-end; 6. Valve Push Rods; 7. Cam Followers; 8. Camshaft; 9. Piston; 10. Gudgeon Pin; 11. Connecting Rod; 12. Combustion Chamber in Piston; 13. Cylinder Liner (sectioned); 14. Cylinder Liner; 15. Engine Block; 16. Cylinder Head Water Space; 17. Inspection Covers; 18. Cylinder Head; 19. Valve Covers.

the A.E.C. 125-b.h.p. engine being used in the two-axle lightweight cars employed on L.M. Region, whilst the equivalent Leyland engine is fitted in pairs to the hydro-mechanical bogie cars of Derby construction placed in service on the Leeds-Bradford route in 1954.

The two types of 150-b.h.p. engine are almost standard fitment with B.R. bogie-type cars built to date, and in the later (50,000) series rolling stock are interchangeable. B.U.T. have also introduced higher horse-power horizontal four-strokes and details of these will be found on later pages. Newcomer to the range is a 275-b.h.p. "six" from the A.E.C. stable and it is of interest to note that both the 230-h.p. Leyland design and the latest A.E.C. have been developed expressly for the B.U.T. rail-traction range.

The B.U.T.–Leyland engines are generally similar to that just described and a close-up of one of the engine cylinders may be seen in Fig. 40, illustrating the location of the injector (1), valve and valve seat insert (3), as well as the cylinder liners (14) which are shoulder located and of the dry type. These liners are a press-fit and may easily be removed and inserted with the aid of special tools. To the right of this illustration may be seen a pair of cam followers (7) commonly referred to as "tappets," and the push-rods (6) one of which has its upper cup-shaped end engaged with the adjustable ball of the valve rocker (5). This illustration shows the engine in the vertical position as the unit is fitted in an engine repair "stand"—although it is of the horizontal type.

The Leyland rocker gear is lubricated by an intermittent feed from the second and fifth camshaft bearings through horizontal oil ways drilled in the engine block and heads (see Fig. 40) via the centre rocker-shaft support bracket on each head and so along the tubular rocker shafts (4) to the rocker levers. A hole drilled in each rocker lever carries a supply of oil to the top of the rocker, thus lubricating the contact surfaces between the valve cap and rocker lever. Oil is returned from the valve operating gear through two external pipes from the tappet gallery to the inner sump.

Fig. 41 illustrates a pair of valves in position in a B.U.T.–Leyland cylinder head and it will be observed that they are seated on stellite valve seat inserts. The valves themselves are stellite faced and have hard chrome-plated stems. It should be noted that the inlet valve (on the right) is larger than the exhaust valve. Note also the long valve guides employed to ensure correct alignment, and the twin coil springs used to return the valves to the closed position. A spring collar, together with a pair of valve cones, holds the spring in the correct position. (See Fig. 42).

The type of injector fitted to the Leyland engine is fully described in Chapter Three and illustrated in Fig. 23 and the valve timing will be

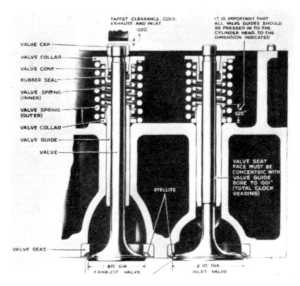

VALVE CAP
VALVE COLLAR
VALVE CONE
RUBBER SEAL
VALVE SPRING (INNER)
VALVE SPRING (OUTER)
VALVE COLLAR
VALVE GUIDE
VALVE

VALVE SEAT

TAPPET CLEARANCE, COLD.
EXHAUST AND INLET
·020.

IT IS IMPORTANT THAT ALL VALVE GUIDES SHOULD BE PRESSED IN TO THE CYLINDER HEAD, TO THE DIMENSION INDICATED

·520″

VALVE SEAT FACE MUST BE CONCENTRIC WITH VALVE GUIDE BORE TO ·001″ (TOTAL CLOCK READING)

STELLITE

1·80″ DIA
EXHAUST VALVE

2·10″ DIA
INLET VALVE

Fig. 41.
Section
through
B.U.T.-
Leyland
Cylinder
Head.

found on page 44. The general layout of this make of engine, in its 150 b.h.p. form, is clearly shown by the part-sectioned view on page 62 and it will be noted that the fuel injection pump is mounted down on the sump face and connected to the injectors by long pipes across the body of the engine. The pump is thus parallel to the engine crankshaft whilst the A.E.C. units have this component at right angles to the crankshaft—see Fig. 35 on page 59.

With a bore of 5 inches and a piston stroke of $5\frac{3}{4}$ inches the "L" engine develops 150 b.h.p. at a speed of 1,800 r.p.m. The compression ratio is 15.75 to 1 and the monobloc casing is made from cast iron into which are inserted the six cylinder liners, also of cast iron; these are "dry" liners, which is to say that their *outer* surfaces do not come into direct contact with the cooling water as is the case with the B.U.T. 230-h.p. engine (page 74). The pistons are of aluminium alloy and mounted on connecting rods by the usual gudgeon pins and phosphor-bronze bushes. A steel forged camshaft is mounted in seven bearings the first and last of which are of leaded gunmetal and the rest of caro-bronze. The crankshaft itself is formed from an alloy steel forging hardened by nitriding and carried in seven main bearings of the "strip" type which are of lead-bronze, indium coated on their wearing surfaces.

The twin oil-pressure switches (Fig. 37, 10) are a common feature on B.U.T. engines and provide an automatic means of stopping the engine should the lubricating oil pressure fall below a pre-determined minimum. The switches are connected to the electric solenoid mentioned on page 35.

PAXMAN HORIZONTAL ENGINE

Among the more powerful six-cylinder horizontal diesel engines capable of being mounted below the floor of railcars is the ZHL series produced by Davey, Paxman & Co. A four-stroke single-acting design based on monobloc construction of crankcase and cylinder block, it has the large (for railcar engines) bore of 7 ins. whilst the piston stroke is $7\frac{3}{4}$ ins.

In normally-aspirated form this engine develops 330 b.h.p. at 1,500 r.p.m. whilst turbo-charged the output is 450 b.h.p. After extensive trials in experimental diesel-electric railcars on the L.M. Region, this type of engine has been adopted for a number of Type 1 800 b.h.p. mixed-traffic locomotives for British Railways.

The ZHL makes use of high strength aluminium alloy for the monobloc casing, the complete engine weighing only a little over 5,000 lbs. whilst many of its components are interchangeable with the larger Paxman engines. Each cylinder head is fitted with four valves and the valve seat inserts are of aluminium-bronze.

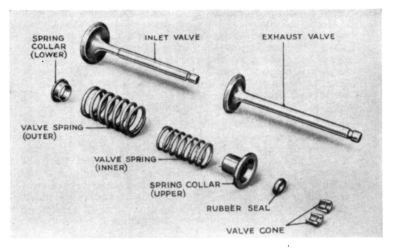

Fig. 42. Poppet valve assemblies as used in B.U.T.-Leyland railcar engine designs.

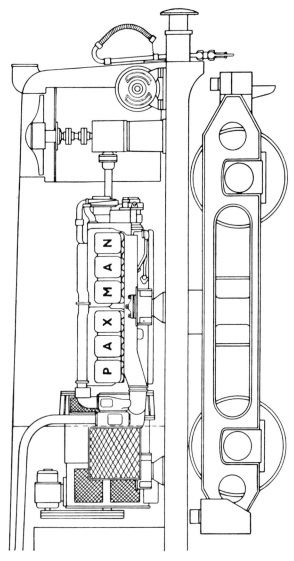

Fig. 43. Installation of Paxman ZH engine in centre-cab twin-engined 900 b.h.p. mixed traffic diesel-electric locomotive.

PAXMAN

The camshaft runs in an oil bath and the cam followers are of the roller-fitted type. Two lubricating oil pumps are employed, one to supply oil in the normal way to the working parts, whilst the second forces lubricant at low pressure through the radiator.

The "flat" design when used for centre-cab locomotives permits a reduced bonnet height and thus offers minimum obstruction to the driver's view. The illustration shows one half of a twin-engined diesel-electric locomotive of this type and it can be seen how well the Paxman ZHL diesel fits into the scheme.

ROLLS-ROYCE ENGINES

The B.U.T. engines described arecapable of developing 150 b.h.p. at the high speed of 1,800 r.p.m. and are developments of successful road transport units. In order to provide greater power output several larger British horizontal railcar engines have been produced and fitted into British Railways diesel cars, the Rolls-Royce six- and eight-cylinder designs and the B.U.T. 230-b.h.p. engine being notable.

The six-cylinder Rolls-Royce engine (see Fig. 44) is fitted to several Metropolitan-Cammell diesel-mechanical cars, whilst the eight-cylinder unit is installed in Derby-built railcars and Craven's single-engined units together with hydraulic transmissions. Both these engines are normally aspirated and four-stroke single-acting types with the cylinders inclined at $17\frac{1}{2}$ degrees to the horizontal. A standard cylinder bore of 5.125 inches and stroke of 6 inches is used. The C6.NFLH, as supplied to B.R., develops 180 b.h.p. at 1,800 r.p.m. and a feature of the layout is that access to all the components requiring periodical attention is obtained from the flanks of the engine and not from above, as the top of the unit is usually close to frame members, etc. Left and right hand views of the C6 engine are shown on the following page.

C.A.V. injection equipment is fitted, the injection pump (20) being mounted on the engine crankcase and fitted with a hydraulic all-speed governor (11). The forced lubrication is by means of a gear-type pressure and scavenge pump driven from the wheelcase (15) gear train. A box type crankcase breather (2) containing a nylon filtering element, allows internal gases to escape to atmosphere. A heat exchanger is fitted by means of which heat in the lubricating oil is transferred to the cooling water, thus enabling the oil to be maintained at its optimum working temperature under all running conditions.

The cooling water flows from the radiator to the circulating pump (8) from where it is directed via the heat exchanger to an inlet gallery on the crankcase and, after circulating around the cylinder block and cylinder

Fig. 44. Rolls-Royce six-cylinder horizontal engine.

Fig. 45. Rolls-Royce six-cylinder normally-aspirated horizontal railcar engine, viewed from cylinder head side.
(KEYS ON OPPOSITE PAGE)

heads, is returned to the radiator. The circulating water pump is driven by a gear in the wheelcase gear train, whilst the hour-counter (9) is driven from an extension of the auxiliary drive gearshaft operating the fuel injection pump (20). The cooling water thermostat (14) is self-contained and located at the front end of the water outlet pipe (16), being so designed as to ensure that when water from the engine is below a selected temperature it does *not* pass through the radiator but is passed, by means of a by-pass pipe, direct to the pump for re-circulation—this pipe can be clearly seen in Fig. 45 connecting items (14) and (8). The main bearings are steel backed shell-form types which support a nitrided crankshaft. A torsion vibration damper of the viscous type is fitted to the crankshaft and the cylinder liners are of the "wet" type. Replaceable valve seats of the press fit variety are utilised in the cylinder heads.

The light alloy pistons each have three compression and one oil-scraper rings. Full-flow lubricating oil filters (3) are mounted adjacent to the f.i. pump, the fuel oil filters (1) are fitted close to the rear of the pump. The electric starter motor (17) is mounted low down on the cylinder head side of the engine and the basic design of the unit permits the disposition of the various auxiliaries to be quite flexible to suit various railcar applications.

The eight-cylinder version of the Rolls-Royce horizontal engine has a similar layout and as applied to B.R. cars develops 238 b.h.p. at 1,880 r.p.m. These engines together with Rolls-Royce torque converters (Twin Disc) are used in Derby-built cars for the Eastern and London Midland Regions' Lea Valley and St. Pancras suburban schemes. Both six- and eight-cylinder engines are available in supercharged form and in fact two C6 blown engines were installed in a standard British Railways (Metro. Cammell) railcar. At 1,800 r.p.m. these units develop 230 b.h.p. The mounting for the blower-unit is shown at 25 on Fig. 45.

B.U.T. 275 B.H.P. RAILCAR ENGINE

A product of the A.E.C. organisation, the B.U.T. six-cylinder 1,100 cubic inch railcar engine shown in Fig. 46 represents the latest unit for railway traction from Southall Works. The maximum output of 275 b.h.p. is produced at a speed of 1,900 r.p.m. and the engine represents a departure

KEY TO FIGS. 44 and 45 (Opposite).

1. Fuel Filters; 2. Crankcase Breather; 3. Lub. Oil Filters; 4. Filter By-Pass Valve; 5. Lub. Oil Pressure Relief Valve; 6. Power take-off; 7. Inlet from Radiator; 8. Cooling Pump; 9. Hour Counter; 10. Sump Drain Plug; 11. All-speed Hydraulic Governor; 12. Lub. Oil Dipstick; 13. Lub. Oil Filler; 14. Coolant Thermostat Housing; 15. Wheelcase; 16. Coolant Outlet Pipe; 17. Starter Motor; 18. Induction Manifold; 19. Exhaust Manifold; 20. C.A.V. Fuel Injection Pump; 21. C.A.V. Lift Pump; 22. Injectors (six); 23. Valve Covers; 24. Torsion Damper; 25. Mounting for Blower (when required).

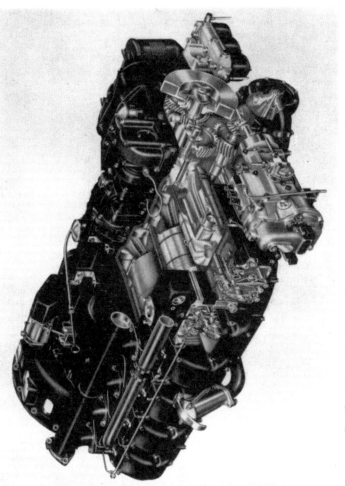

Fig. 46. B.U.T.-A.E.C. 275 b.h.p. six cylinder horizontal engine as used on Netherlands Railways.

from previous Southall practice in that individual cylinder heads are employed—each with two exhaust and two inlet valves. Further, the design features "wet" cylinder liners but retains the standard A.E.C. railcar engine arrangement of mounting the fuel injection pump at right angles to the crankshaft.

A cylinder bore of 6⅛ inches combined with a piston stroke of 6⅛ inches gives the "square" dimensions which have become popular in automotive practice. The AH1100, as it is termed, is a four-stroke cycle engine employing direct injection and the design includes a crankshaft torsional vibration damper. The engine casing is of "monobloc" construction as on previous A.E.C. railcar designs, with the usual sump and sump extension. The cylinder heads, however, feature several interesting departures from previous practice. The copper sheaths, into which the injectors fit, are in direct contact with the cooling water whilst each pair of valves are operated through a single rocker. The lubrication system follows normal standards but includes a full-flow externally-mounted filter system.

Engines of this series have been successfully employed to power diesel-electric railcars on the Netherlands Railways—replacing earlier types of A.E.C. underfloor engines already described on other pages. Exhaust turbo-charging the AH1100 unit increases the output to 360 b.h.p.

B.U.T. 230 B.H.P. RAILCAR ENGINE

On the page following is illustrated the 230-b.h.p. B.U.T. engine produced by Leyland for rail traction and fitted to cars of the Derby 63 ft. 6 in. 50,000 series. This engine is a horizontal six-cylinder four-stroke and is not super-charged as far as applications to B.R. cars are concerned. The engines are used in pairs in place of the usual 150-b.h.p. type and have cylinders of 5½ inches bore and a piston stroke of 6½ inches. The maximum speed is 1,900 r.p.m. and the disposition of auxiliary equipment is generally similar to the other B.U.T.–Leyland units. Monobloc construction is employed but the cylinder liners are of the "wet" pattern with their outer surfaces in direct contact with the cooling water circulating through the engine block.

Pistons, connecting rods, crank and camshafts are all of orthodox design. The lubrication system is interesting in so far as there are two separate pumps mounted one at each side of the engine. At the front end is a pressure pump of the gear-type which provides lubricant under pressure to all vital points, whilst at the rear end of the sump a scavenge pump is fitted to transfer oil from the sump well to the main sump at the front of the engine. An integral oil cooler or heat exchanger is a feature of this engine and a large capacity lubricating oil filter of the centrifugal type is also employed. A turbo-charged version of this engine is fitted to several

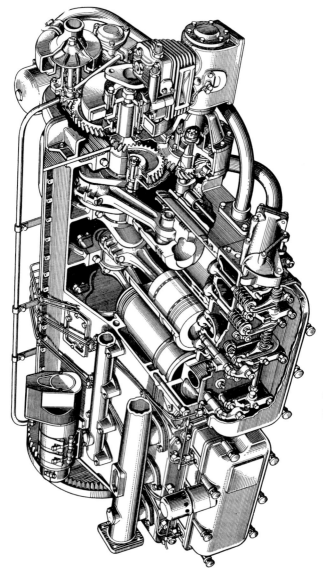

Fig. 47. B.U.T.-Leyland 230 b.h.p. six-cylinder horizontal engine.

railcars in operation on Ulster Transport Authority lines and the engine in this form develops 275 b.h.p. at 1,900 r.p.m.

MAYBACH MD650 ENGINE (*See Fig.* 48)

In the United Kingdom the Maybach range of high-speed engines is manufactured by Bristol Siddeley Engines Ltd., under licences from Maybach Motorenbau of Friedrichshafen. The engines are high power, light weight, having a 1,500 r.p.m. maximum operating speed and are fitted in line service locomotives of Swindon-built twin-engined 2,300–2,700 h.p. diesel-hydraulic type. The Beyer Peacock (Hymek) 1,700 h.p. diesel-hydraulic locomotives (see page 132) are powered by a single MD870 V-16 engine, whilst the Brush "Falcon" 2,800 h.p. diesel-electric locomotive is powered by two MD655 V-12 engines. These 12 cylinder Maybach engines are similar to those in the 2,700 h.p. diesel-hydraulics being exhaust turbo-charged and charge-cooled.

The MD650 is a "Vee" form engine having twelve cylinders in two banks of six and is a single-acting four-stroke design which, as applied to W.R. locomotives, develops 1,135 b.h.p. at 1,530 r.p.m. The cylinder bore is 7.3 ins. and piston stroke 7.9 ins. These engines are turbo-pressure charged by means of a vertically mounted unit of Maybach design which can be seen in the illustration (fitted to the top of the structure). The cylinder liners are of the "wet" type and each cylinder has an individual head carrying three inlet and three exhaust valves arranged around an almost spherical combustion chamber located centrally in the cylinder head. A single unit injector is fitted to each cylinder head, the pump being combined with the injection valve in a unit operated directly from the inlet camshaft through a rocker arm. The operation of the triple valve groups is achieved by means of a pair of overhead camshafts and small rocker arms for each bank of cylinders. The camshafts are driven by a train of helical gears from the crankshaft. Automatic hydraulic adjustment is provided to retain perfect valve clearance independent of regular attention and to reduce noise to a minimum.

Speed regulation is performed by means of a regulator fitted at the power end of the engine and designed as a centrifugal flyweight governor connected to the unit injectors by adjustable linkage. Use is made of lubricating oil pressure to operate a servo mechanism and at the same time act as a safety device for the engine. Forced feed lubrication for the 650 engine is made up of three separate circuits: scavenge lubricating oil; main lubrication, and piston cooling. Oil pumps contained in the base of the crankcase are driven from the crankshaft by spur gearing. Immediately the engine starting switch is closed an oil priming pump is put into operation but only when sufficient oil pressure is built up in the engine can the starter be brought into action.

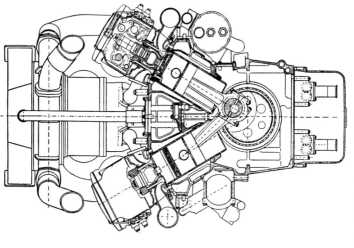

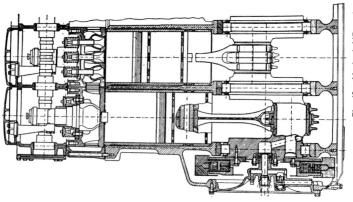

Fig. 48. Maybach MD engine of "V" type. (Longitudinal and cross sections.)

Outstanding feature of the Maybach engine is the single-piece " tunnel " crankcase Fig. 49, and the completely assembled crankshaft is introduced " tunnel-wise " into the crankcase from the front end of the engine.

76

HIGH SPEED ENGINES

In this Maybach engine the main objective has been to attain high speeds with running performance hitherto obtained only with the best slow speed engines. Oil for piston cooling reaches the pistons by means of telescopic pipes, being forced directly to and through the pistons, led at high speed over the undersides of the piston crowns and especially round the piston ring grooves. After cooling has been achieved the oil is free to flow out downwards through an opening below the

Fig. 49. Maybach crankcase.

piston crown lubricating the gudgeon pin on the way. The oil is cooled in a heat-exchanger before being recirculated.

The MD650 crankshaft is disc-webbed, which is to say that two adjacent crankwebs of a normal shaft design are joined together to form one solid disc (Fig. 50), the rim of this disc forms the inner race for a large diameter roller type bearing the outer race of which is mounted in the walls of the crankcase tunnel.

Fig. 50. Maybach crankshaft.

Connecting rods are of the fork and blade type with the main rod supported on the crankpin and the blade rod working on a plain bearing fitted to the exterior of the main rod bearing (Fig. 51).

Each piston is fitted with three compression rings and two oil scraper rings, as mentioned previously they are oil cooled from a separate lubricating oil circuit and it will be seen from Fig. 52 that the pistons are designed with detachable crowns.

Fig. 51. Maybach connecting rod assembly (main rod on right).

Fig. 52.
Maybach
oil-cooled
pistons.

78

PAXMAN "VENTURA" ENGINE

Contrasting with the well-established medium-speed range produced by Davey, Paxman & Co. Ltd. (see page 50), is the new "Ventura" series of high-speed lightweight diesels designated type YJ. The aim has been to achieve a high power-to-weight ratio which is well-suited to the limited axle weights of some locomotives. "Ventura" engines have been fitted as alternative power units to Western Region diesel-hydraulic locomotives.

The YJ engine is a turbo-charged "vee" form unit with cylinder banks pitched at 60 degrees and is produced in 12 and 16 cylinder versions both

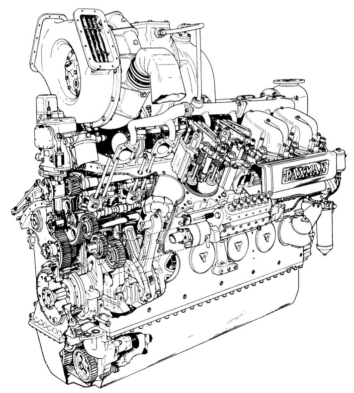

Fig. 53. Paxman "Ventura" 12 YJX engine.

of which have a common cylinder bore of $7\frac{3}{4}$ ins. together with a piston stroke of $8\frac{1}{2}$ ins. A maximum speed of 1,500 r.p.m. gives the 12 cylinder type an output of 1,200–1,400 b.h.p. whilst the 16 cylinder unit produces 1,600 to 1,870 b.h.p.

The extremely compact and light design is largely made possible by a fabricated steel engine housing produced by welding high tensile steel plate and precision steel castings. The crankshaft, forged from nickel-chrome high tensile steel, is a dynamically balanced fully-machined assembly and features an *additional* main bearing at the drive-end, provided to support the weight of the armature of single-bearing electric generators. All auxiliary drives are taken from a gear at the drive-end of the crankshaft.

Each individual cylinder head of aluminium alloy has its injector mounted centrally, whilst the twin exhaust and inlet valves are operated via valve rockers, push rods and cam-followers from a camshaft located between the two cylinder banks. A design point worthy of note is that the cylinder head valve covers have been specially designed to exclude covering the injectors so avoiding dilution of the lubricating oil in the event of a leaking fuel union.

Connecting rods are of the "fork and blade" pattern and the aluminium alloy pistons are oil cooled by a metered supply of lubricant passing up through the rods. The pistons have a cast-iron top ring insert and three compression rings and two oil-control rings are provided.

Unlike the large medium-speed engines which have individual fuel injection pumps, the "Ventura" engine has one monobloc type in-line pump fitted to each side of the engine housing driven by carden shafts from gears at the drive-end of the diesel. A single water pump is provided which directs the coolant to the inlet manifold of each bank of cylinders. Lubricating oil supplies are dealt with by two pumps positioned at the flywheel end of the unit, one supplies high pressure oil to the engine bearings whilst the other circulates the lubricant through the coolers.

CHAPTER SIX

THE DIESEL ENGINE
COOLING SYSTEMS

The diesel cooling system must transfer to the air flow through the radiator the heat absorbed by the engine cooling water but only sufficient heat should be transferred to maintain the most favourable operating conditions and temperatures in the engine independent of load or atmospheric temperature.

LOCOMOTIVE COOLING SYSTEM (*See Fig.* 54)

The diagram shows a typical layout with a vertical six-cylinder engine (A) having a radiator (B) at the leading end of the locomotive's hood. The heavy black lines show the cooling water circuit and starting with the six pipes emerging from the cylinder heads, the water is carried to the top tank of the radiator (C) and having passed through the cooling elements, is drawn along the suction pipe by the water circulating pump (D) from whence it enters the engine to complete the cycle.

The header rank (E) is provided to make up any loss in the system and feeds direct into the water pump suction line whilst in addition a vent is provided from the top tank of the radiator to the header tank. In some designs the fan (F) is driven mechanically by the engine and is entirely dependent on engine speed—irrespective of the coolant or atmospheric temperatures.

SERCK BEHR FAN CONTROL

This system is shown chain-dotted in the illustration. The fan speed is controlled thermostatically and is infinitely variable from standstill to maximum speed, the speed at any moment being determined solely by the coolant temperature at the moment and is independent of varying engine loads or air temperature.

The drive comprises an hydraulic pump driven from the engine and coupled to an hydraulic motor on which the fan is mounted. A controller

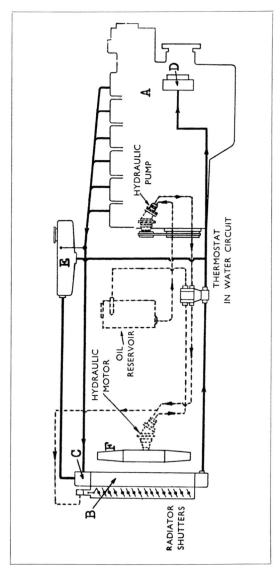

Fig. 54. Locomotive Cooling System with Serck Behr Control System. (Cooling water circuit shown solid lines; hydraulic circuit shown dotted)

sensitive to the coolant temperature, governs the speed of the hydraulic motor by regulating a by-pass in the hydraulic circuit. The fourth component is an oil reservoir which houses magnetic filters. On starting, the hydraulic pump begins to rotate and the hydraulic fluid is wholly by-passed through the controller so that the fan motor does not rotate but when the coolant approaches the pre-selected temperature a thermostatic element in the controller actuates the hydraulic by-pass valve, allowing some of the fluid to pass to the fan motor, which starts to rotate. The speed of the fan increases until there is sufficient cooling to maintain the coolant at the pre-selected temperature and as the load on the engine is increased so the fan runs at a correspondingly greater speed always controlling the coolant at the desired value.

Shutters fitted to the front of the radiator are sometimes operated from the hydraulic system, the pressure from the circuit being led to an hydraulic ram operating the shutters which are arranged to open just as the fan starts to rotate and closed again just as the fan stops rotating. The shutters close when no cooling is required and help to maintain stable temperatures in the cooling system.

MAIN LINE LOCO. COOLING SYSTEM (*See Fig.* 55)

In this system the twin radiators are mounted at an angle in the roof-sides of the locomotive and are fan-cooled. The header tank is also accommodated in the roof. The coolant (treated water) is circulated by a pump which delivers it to a distributor from whence it passes through the exhaust elbows to the exhaust manifolds, after which it enters the driving ends of the cylinder blocks to cool the combustion zone and the exhaust end of the cylinder liners. From the cylinder blocks the coolant passes to the outlet and to a thermostatic valve.

If, at this point, the coolant is cold, (below 165° F.), the thermostatic valve directs the coolant back to the inlet of the coolant pump but when the temperature rises to the disigned operating figure (165° to 180° F.), the thermostatic valve gradually changes the flow (as shown in the inset) so that it passes through the radiators to maintain the engine's operating temperature.

The roof mounted header tank maintains the system full but should the coolant in this tank drop to the minimum permissible level a float switch stops the engine. The engine is stopped also if the flow of coolant, (which closes the electrical contacts of the coolant flow switch) drops to a pre-determined value. If, during a run, the temperature of the coolant rises to 184° F., a temperature switch is operated which brightens a *fault* light in the cab and the *water* light on each cubicle. The main power handle should, under these conditions, be eased back to allow the coolant

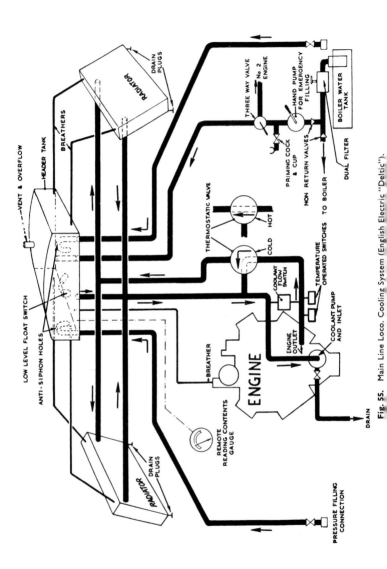

Fig. 55. Main Line Loco. Cooling System (English Electric "Deltic").

temperature to drop, thus dimming the indicator lights. If, however, the coolant temperature continues to rise to 195°F., a second temperature switch stops the engine.

RAILCAR COOLING SYSTEM (*See Fig.* 56)

The example illustrates one complete engine system consisting of a radiator (C) with separate header tank (B) fan (E) which is shaft-driven from the engine via drive pulley (L), a thermostat (K) to maintain the correct coolant temperature and belt-driven water pump (F) to circulate the coolant. The system is of the "full-flow" type in which the header tank is directly in the cooling circuit. Some railcars are fitted with the header tank "out of circuit" and a single pipe connects with the cooling system.

The pump (F) draws coolant from the base of the radiator (C) and delivers it to the engine via the lubricating oil cooler (D). From the pump the coolant flows to the front end of the engine block (M) to circulate around the cylinders and then passes into the cylinder heads. After leaving the front head (A) the coolant enters the thermostat where, depending on temperature, it circulates directly to the engine via the by-pass pipe (J) or through the header tank to the radiator and thence back to the engine. The body of the thermostat contains two ports, one leads to the radiator and the other to the by-pass pipe. A capsule containing temperature sensitive liquid or gas is secured to one end of the thermostat body in a position that will cause the by-pass to be closed when the unit has fully expanded and operated its valves.

A float-switch (G) is incorporated in the header tank and should the coolant fall to a dangerous level operates to shut down the engine electrically through a stop solenoid on the fuel injection pump. When the engine is cold the radiator is by-passed due to the action of the thermostat and all coolant flows directly to the pump and thence to the engine. As the coolant temperature rises the capsule expands and at a temperature of approximately 75 degrees Centigrade it has expanded sufficiently to cause the valve to move off its seat permitting some of the coolant to flow to the radiator. The coolant continues to rise in temperature and the capsule continues to expand moving the valve further from its seat thus increasing the flow through the radiator and decreasing the flow through the by-pass pipe. When a constant temperature of 85–90 degrees Centigrade has been reached the by-pass port is conpletely closed ensuring a full flow through the header tank and radiator.

The header tank which ensures replacement of any loss in the system, has a filler cap (H) which is located in the side of the railcar body. An overflow pipe or vent (I) is incorporated in the header design. On some systems

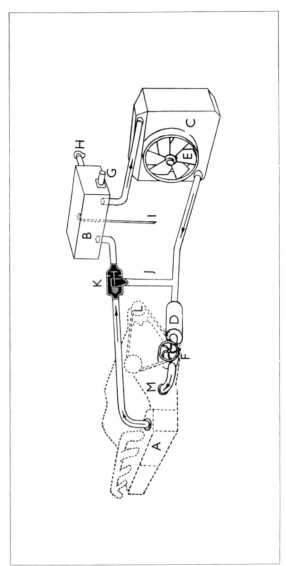

Fig. 56 Railcar engine cooling system (Full-flow type).

the header tank filler cap is sealed and the tank itself is open to atmosphere only through small relief valves placed in the crown of the tank, this type of system being termed " pressurised."

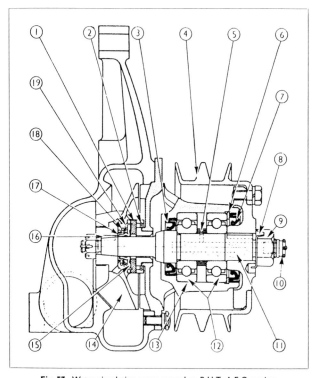

Fig. 57. Water circulating pump as used on B.U.T.-A.E.C. engine.

1.	Carbon Seating.	10.	Lubricator.
2.	Spring Ring.	11.	Pump Spindle.
3.	Grease Retainer.	12.	Ball Bearings.
4.	Drive Pulley.	13.	Bearing Housing.
5.	Distance Collar.	14.	Impeller.
6.	Circlip	15.	Rubber Seal.
7.	Grease Retainer.	16.	Key.
8.	Tab Washer.	17.	Distance Ring.
9.	Lock Nut.	18.	Gland Spring.
	19.	Housing.	

TORQUE CONVERTER COOLING

Torque converters which are described in Chapters 9 and 10 also have a bearing on locomotive and railcar cooling systems and it is opportune to illustrate them now.

Where torque converter transmissions are employed additional cooling must be provided for the converter fluid which has to be maintained at an operating temperature around 180–220 degrees Farenheit and even higher under extreme conditions.

Converter fluid flow is maintained by a charging pump and is passed through a heat exchanger in the engine coolant circuit (additional to the engine-oil heat exchanger (D) in Fig. 56.) The radiator capacity must of course be sufficient to cool both engine and torque converter under all service conditions.

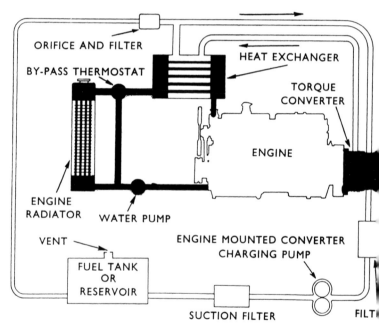

Fig. 58. Torque converter cooling diagram. (White pipes—converter fluid circuit; B pipes—engine coolant circuit.)

CHAPTER SEVEN

THE DIESEL ENGINE
LUBRICATION SYSTEMS

Mention has been made from time to time of the lubricating oil systems of engines described and it is now opportune to treat this important matter in more detail.

Friction is a force which does its level best to prevent movement between two surfaces in contact. Lubrication reduces the friction of these rubbing surfaces (at the same time reducing wear) by placing between them a suitable liquid substance.

Generally, the lubricating oil systems of diesel engines can be divided into two types—Wet Sump and Dry Sump. In the wet sump system, the crankcase serves as an oil reservoir and must be of sufficient depth to ensure that the suction side of the lubricating oil pump is not uncovered when the railcar or locomotive is in motion. With the dry sump pattern a main reservoir is usually located below or at the side of the crankcase.

The oil is pumped from the crankcase or reservoir by a pump driven from the engine crankshaft and passed at a pressure ranging from 5–30 lbs. per sq. in. to an oil cooler. The oil cooler (or "heat exchanger") may be either water or air cooled. On leaving the cooler the lubricant is routed to a main oil gallery which runs the length of the engine usually in the top half of the crankcase. From the gallery feeds are taken direct to each of the main crankshaft bearings from where, by means of suitable drillings and hollow pins, the lubricant reaches the big-end journals. A further stage is reached when from the crankpins the lubricant travels by way of passages in the connecting rods to the small-end bearings.

In many designs an oil spray or jet from the gudgeon pins is arranged to provide partial piston cooling, whilst on some units a similar jet from the big-end bearings provides "splash" lubrication to the cylinder liners. Ultimately the lubricating oil escapes from the bearings and working parts and finds its way back into the sump (or reservoir) and is then ready for recirculation.

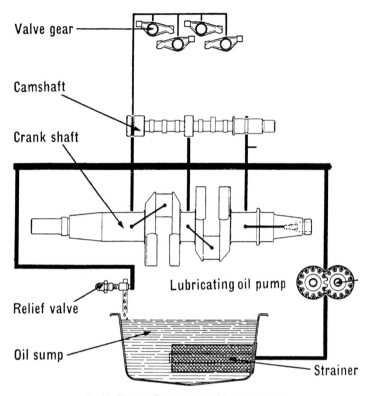

Valve gear

Camshaft

Crank shaft

Lubricating oil pump

Relief valve

Oil sump

Strainer

Fig. 59. Diagram of wet sump type lubrication system.

Naturally, it is of vital importance that the lubricant be properly purified and the two main systems employed are "full flow" filtration in which all the oil is filtered and "by-pass" filtering in which only part of the oil is diverted through the filtration unit. At a suitable location in the system, there is provided a spring-loaded pressure-relief valve which is set to open at a particular pressure and relieve any excess accumulation which may occur.

Lubricating the pistons and cylinders is a much more difficult problem than the lubrication of bearings and gears. As already mentioned, the lubrication of the cylinders is usually by "splash", suitable oil-scraper rings being provided to ensure that under-lubrication is prevented. These slotted scraper rings through the medium of holes drilled through the

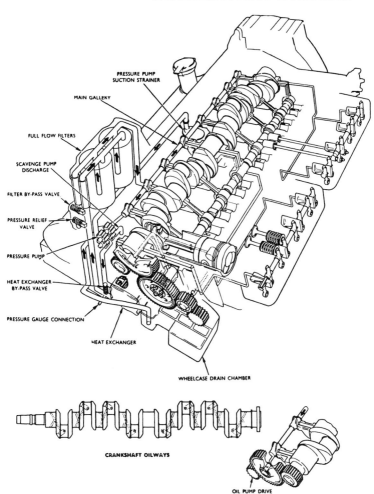

PRESSURE PUMP
SUCTION STRAINER

MAIN GALLERY

FULL FLOW FILTERS

SCAVENGE PUMP
DISCHARGE

FILTER BY-PASS VALVE

PRESSURE RELIEF
VALVE

PRESSURE PUMP

HEAT EXCHANGER
BY-PASS VALVE

PRESSURE GAUGE CONNECTION

HEAT EXCHANGER

WHEELCASE DRAIN CHAMBER

CRANKSHAFT OILWAYS

OIL PUMP DRIVE

OIL FLOW TO No. I MAIN BEARING
AND SECONDARY IDLER GEAR

Fig. 60. Rolls-Royce 8-cylinder horizontal engine—lubricating oil circuit.

piston skirt, keep the oil consumption to a minimum by preventing it actually reaching the combustion space.

RAILCAR ENGINE LUBRICATION (*See Fig.* 60)

A typical railcar engine lubrication system is that of the Rolls-Royce C8 horizontal unit shown in the illustration. This is a wet sump system and provides pressure lubrication to all bearings, cylinders and gears and in addition a metered supply to the valve mechanism and air compressor.

The oil pump assembly is gear-driven off the front end of the crankshaft and incorporates a pressure pump and a scavenge pump. Residue oil from the wheelcase drain-chamber is returned to the sump by the scavenge pump.

The oil is drawn by the pressure pump from the sump through a submerged strainer and is delivered directly to a heat-exchanger which heats or cools the oil to its working temperature by the transfer of heat from or to the engine coolant. From the heat-exchanger the oil passes through the full-flow external filters, the main bearings and the rest of the system.

Immediately before the filters is a by-pass valve and a pressure-relief valve which protect the filters and the oil system as a whole from excessive oil pressure under cold conditions. The external oil filters are of the replaceable element type and are positioned on the engine to give easy access. An oil pressure safety switch is fitted which shuts down the engine in event of abnormally low oil pressure.

It will be noticed from the inset to the illustration that the crankshaft is drilled to provide oilways between the main journals and crankpins. On some horizontal railcar engines the lubricating oil is filtered through a centrifuge externally mounted on the engine crankcase—one of these units can be clearly seen in the illustration on page 74 at the top right hand corner.

DELTIC ENGINE LUBRICATION

On the opposite page is shown the lubricating oil system of an English Electric "Deltic" engine (refer to pages 53 and 54) as employed in British Railways Type 5 locomotives. For clarity only one cylinder bank of the three is shown.

It will be seen that with the engine in operation, oil is taken by the pressure pump from the service tank and is forced through the filters to the crankshaft main bearings, big-end bearings and pistons. The oil also proceeds to the camshaft and flexible shaft through restrictors whilst a metered allowance is sent to the scavenge blower bearings.

The used oil which afterwards drains back into the engine sump is drawn by the scavenge pump to a thermostatic valve and if it is cold (i.e. below 135° F.) the valve will direct the oil back into the service tank via

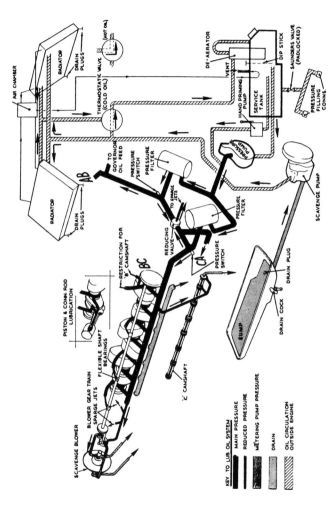

Fig. 61. Lubrication system of English Electric "Deltic" engine as used in British Railways Type 5 diesel-electric locomotives.

the de-aerator. When the oil has reached a predetermined temperature setting (135° to 150° F.) the thermostatic valve will direct the oil through the radiators and then back through the valve into the service tank—the two possible routings being clearly shown in the illustration. A hand priming pump is provided so that oil can be passed from the service tank to the output side of the pressure pump if required.

It will be seen from the above that the system employed is similar to that encountered on the A.E.C. 150 b.h.p. engines where the sump acts as a chamber for the scavenge pump to draw on to replenish the reservoir. It will also be noted that on the Deltic engine the lubricating oil is cooled by air whereas in the case of the horizontal railcar engines the medium was water.

CHAPTER EIGHT

FLUID AND OTHER COUPLINGS

RAILCAR FLUID COUPLING

THE FLUID FLYWHEEL consists of three main components—the flywheel proper, the driving member (M) and the driven member (L). The flywheel is bolted to the engine crankshaft and also carries the driving member. The driven member or "runner" is free to rotate within the casing formed by the other two parts and carries the coupling flange to which is attached the transmission shaft. The runner is carried on two bearings, one within the engine crankshaft flange (N) and the other in the rear of the driving member (P).

The driving and driven members are each equipped with radial webs forming pockets on their *inner* surfaces and the space within is filled with engine oil to the level of the uppermost plug (K). An oil seal (R) is fitted to the rear of the driving member where the driven member shaft (Q) protrudes and is of the self-adjusting "bellows" type—a packingless gland.

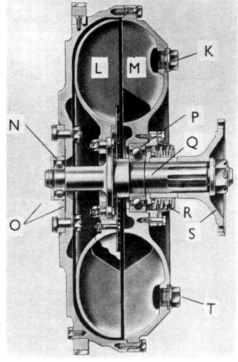

Fig. 62. B.U.T. Railcar Hydraulic Coupling.
K. Filler Plug; L. Driven Member; M. Driving Member; N. Spigot Bearing; O. Engine Crankshaft; P. Shaft Bearing; Q. Shaft; R. Gland; S. Driving Flange; T. Filler Plug.

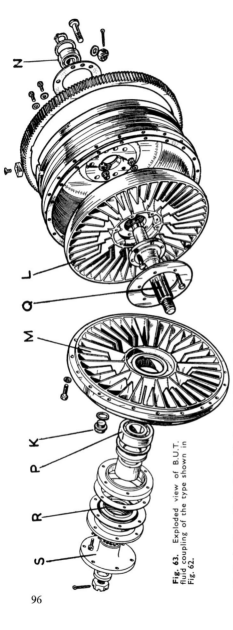

N

L

Q

M

K

P

R

S

Fig. 63. Exploded view of B.U.T. fluid coupling of the type shown in Fig. 62.

The fluid coupling is in fact an automatic clutch and transmits power to the drive shaft in accordance with the speed of the diesel. At engine idling speed the coupling does not transmit power but a small increase of speed is sufficient to cause the fluid coupling to function in a slight manner. Further increases of engine speed ensure full transmission of power.

It will be seen that when the driving member commences to turn at speed the oil is forced under pressure, into the pockets of the driven member which itself commences to rotate until both members are locked together in one unit. The two units are in no way connected *except by the oil* and should a seizure occur in the engine or transmission the oil is immediately "tearable", thus preventing serious damage. The fluid coupling is not subject to wear and tear like a normal friction clutch and cannot work out of adjustment. Should the driving member of a fluid coupling revolve faster than the driven one, the condition is known as "slip" and this is duly allowed for in the coupling design whilst accelerating —it should however, be virtually absent when the engine is at full throttle.

96

RAILCAR STEP-CIRCUIT COUPLING

With British Railways railcars of higher horse power, such as those propelled by twin B.U.T. or Rolls-Royce 230 h.p. engines, readers will observe a different type fluid coupling. This is the step-circuit 550 STC type manufactured by Fluidrive Engineering Co. Ltd.

These steel traction couplings have a stepped reservoir circuit and as will be seen from the illustration (Fig. 64), the impeller and casing are rotated by the engnie crankshaft whilst the runner and output shaft are connected to the transmission. No mechanical connection exists between the impeller and runner, both of which have radial vanes.

The impeller has a reservoir or ante-chamber placed within its centre and under normal running conditions this chamber is kept empty of liquid by centrifugal force—the fluid being concentrated in the pockets on the outside extremities of the impeller and runner.

When, however, the runner is under near-stalling conditions (as, for example, when the engine is idling in gear or when starting) there is little or no centrifugal force acting within the runner and so the ante-chamber is filled with liquid. The result is that the mass of liquid in circulation between impeller and runner is reduced thus lowering the "drag" and reducing the tendency for the railcar to "creep". In addition, fuel consumption, when idling, is cut down.

When the engine is accelerated and the runner also increases speed, the liquid is returned from the ante-chamber by centrifugal force to complete the filling of the normal working circuit.

FREEWHEEL COUPLING (*See Fig*. 65)

Freewheel type couplings are installed in railcars to allow coasting on down grades without the transmission driving the diesel engine. A B.U.T. type freewheel is illustrated although there are several other designs in use for mechanical drive rail vehicles.

The illustration shows the freewheel built into a transmission shaft assembly equipped with two universal type couplings employing needle roller bearings. The action of the freewheel can be observed by reference to Fig. 66. When the driving shaft rotates in the clockwise direction indicated by the arrow, the rollers are driven up hard against the driven unit by the wedge-shaped faces, thus locking the freewheel into a solid coupling. When, however, the driven unit rotates faster than the drive shaft—as for instance when the railcar is running down-grade under low throttle—the rollers fall back into the grooves prepared for them and assume the position indicated by the dotted lines in the sketch. This action enables the transmission to outrun the engine and avoids driving the engine from the wheels.

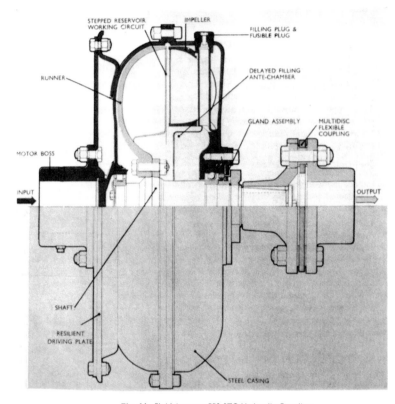

STEPPED RESERVOIR
WORKING CIRCUIT

IMPELLER

FILLING PLUG &
FUSIBLE PLUG

DELAYED FILLING
ANTE-CHAMBER

RUNNER

GLAND ASSEMBLY

MULTIDISC
FLEXIBLE
COUPLING

MOTOR BOSS

INPUT

OUTPUT

SHAFT

RESILIENT
DRIVING PLATE

STEEL CASING

Fig. 64. Fluidrive type 550 STC Hydraulic Coupling.

UNIVERSAL COUPLING (*See Fig.* 67)

To take movement between resiliently mounted units (as, for instance, between engine and gearbox, which are both suspended in rubber bonded units on railcars) and to overcome the movement of bogies on curves and crossings, most drive shafts are fitted with universal couplings and sliding splined portions which allow for extension and compression of the coupling's centres.

Today, most of the rail traction universals employ needle-roller type bearings although the plain phosphor-bronze bush pattern is sometimes seen. The principal parts of the Hardy Spicer needle-roller bearing

98

COUPLINGS

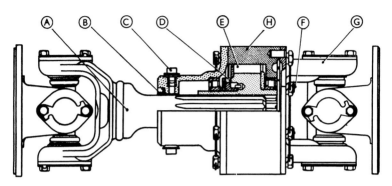

Fig. 65. Propeller Shaft used between Fluid Coupling and Gearbox incorporating Freewheel. (B.U.T.)

A. Propeller Shaft; B. Seal; C. Lubricating Plug; D. Freewheel Cam; E. Freewheel Rollers; F. Lubricator; G. Universal Joint Assembly; H. Freewheel Cage.

universal coupling may be seen on the next page and this particular joint is of a series used on the multiple-unit trains of British Railways.

Twelve of these universal couplings are used on a British Railways m.u. railcar and their location may be traced on page 136—two on the propeller shaft, two on the freewheel shaft and two on the fan-drive shaft. These are doubled for the twin engine-transmission sets.

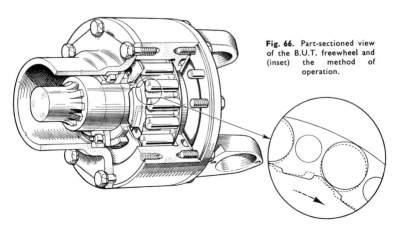

Fig. 66. Part-sectioned view of the B.U.T. freewheel and (inset) the method of operation.

It will be observed that the main components consist of a "star" or cruciform-piece two legs of which are fitted to the yoke mounted on the end of the shaft and the other two legs to the coupling flange itself. The needle roller bearing assemblies are mounted over each leg and form the connecting links between the three main components. Special end-plates and gaskets are used to retain the lubricant within the roller bearings. Universal couplings of this type are manufactured from quite small sizes, such as those used to drive the radiator fans of railcars, up to large series employed for transmitting the main drive of diesel-hydraulic line locomotives—but the principle is the same as that illustrated in the view below. A typical application of the universal is that shown by "G" in Fig. 65, which also, incidentally, clearly shows a splined sliding shaft arrangement.

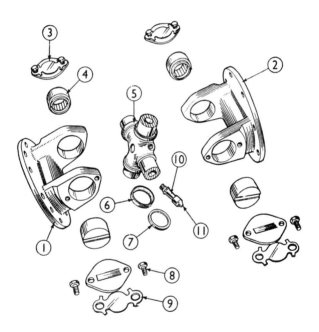

Fig. 67. Universal joint—shown exploded.

1.	Output flange.	7.	Star piece gasket.
2.	Input flange.	8.	Screw for bearing cover.
3.	Bearing cover.	9.	Lockplate for screws.
4.	Needle roller bearing.	10.	Lubricator extention.
5.	Star piece.	11.	Lubricator nipple.
6.	Gasket retainer.		

CHAPTER NINE

THE TRANSMISSION SYSTEM

LOCOMOTIVES

UNLIKE STEAM LOCOMOTIVES which are self-starting and employ direct drive to the wheels, the power from a diesel engine is transmitted to the axles through one of several forms of transmission. The transmitting medium may be of the mechanical, hydro-mechanical, hydraulic or electric type. There are several other combinations but we are not concerned with those here.

The Fell locomotive of British Railways, No. 10100, was an example of the mechanical transmission system and was equipped with four Paxman 500 b.h.p. engines, the power from which was transmitted through a Vulcan-Sinclair fluid coupling on each engine to a gearbox and thence to the eight drive wheels which were coupled together by side rods. There are a considerable number of low-powered shunting locomotives with mechanical transmission now at work on British Railways.

Transmission systems which employ hydraulic means are often designed with a mechanical (friction) drive when the running speed has reached about 70 per cent. of the maximum and are, therefore, actually hydro-mechanical designs. Several examples of the hydraulic transmission have appeared in new locomotives now operating on British Railways. However, in dealing with practical considerations, apart from several diesel mechanical units mentioned above, honours go to the diesel-electric drive which has been very successfully employed in the shunting field in Britain for well over twenty years. It is with this form of transmission that we shall deal in some detail, as most readers are likely to come into contact with it early in their "diesel careers". On the Southern Region the diesel will be employed only with electric transmission, whether for shunting, main line or multiple-unit cars.

ELECTRIC TRANSMISSION—DEFINITIONS

Before proceeding to deal with diesel-electric units it is essential that basic electrical terms be understood. On the following pages will be found the more common terms together with brief explanations.

Electricity—is a form of energy and takes various forms—power, lighting and heating for example. Electricity can be produced by a generator, by a battery or by friction. "Static" electricity produced by the latter method is of little commercial use.

Electric Current—this is a flow of electrons (*negative* charges of electricity from the negative terminal of a generator through a circuit to the positive terminal for example).

Generator—if insulated wire is wound around a wrought iron bar and the ends connected to a battery, the bar becomes a magnet and it sets up a magnetic field. If the very opposite takes place and a magnet is moved in and out of a coil, electricity will be generated in the coil. This principle is used in a generator although it is usual to place the magnet around the coil which is revolved inside it.

Circuit—this is the path along which a current may flow. Compare this with water flowing through a pipe—to enable it to flow there must be a difference of pressure and this is measured in lbs. per sq. inch. The water flows at a certain rate measured in gallons per hour; in electricity the pressure is called e.m.f. (electro-motive force) and measured in "volts". The rate at which it flows is measured in "amperes".

Volt—the unit of electrical pressure.

Ampere—the rate of current flow.

Ammeter—an instrument for measuring the magnitude of an electric current in amperes.

Watt—a practical unit of power. One watt of power is conveyed by a steady current of one ampere flowing under a steady pressure of one volt.

Cell—a lead-acid unit in which chemical action takes place and produces a force which causes a movement of electricity (or flow of electrons round the circuit).

Battery—several cells connected so that they unite to supply current to the same circuit.

Resistance—this is the property of a substance by means of which it *resists* the flow of electricity through it, causing a disposal of electrical energy as heat.

Ohm—the measurement of resistance.

Ohm's Law—that a current in a circuit is equal to the voltage divided by the resistance of the circuit.

E.M.F.—electromotive force. This is that force which tends to cause a movement of electricity in a circuit. For instance, in a lead-acid cell the chemical action which takes place produces a force which tends to cause a movement of electricity or flow of electrons round the circuit. This is the e.m.f. of the cell.

102

Insulation—this confines the flow of electricity to desired paths. Materials such as rubber, bakelite, mica, etc. are used as their resistance is so high (millions of ohms) that they prevent any current passing through them.

Electromagnet—in its simplest form a soft iron core around which are wound a number of turns of insulated wire. If an electric current is passed through the wire the device becomes a magnet. The magnetism depends on the current flow and thus the magnet can be switched on and off and its strength controlled.

Armature—the rotating component of a direct current generator or motor.

Brush—a block of conducting material used to make contact with the rotating part of an electrical machine.

Bus-bar—a conductor which is used to establish connection between the incoming and outgoing circuits of an electrical system.

Relay—a switch operated by small electric currents and used to operate apparatus controlling large currents.

Fuse—a device for interrupting an excessive current—containing a length of wire which melts when the current in it exceeds a fixed value.

Flash-over—an arc between two electrical conductors produced accidentally.

Field—a region of space in which a force is excited on a unit magnetic pole.

Earth—a low resistance path (due to failure of insulation) from a live conductor to earthed metal surrounding or near it.

Continuity—the effective electrical contact of all parts of a circuit.

Overload—a load on a machine beyond the rated full load which can be carried for an indefinite time without undue temperature rise.

Overload protection—a device which disconnects the machine when the overload carried by it has raised the machine's temperature beyond the safety limit.

Series connection—circuits are connected in series when the same current flows through all of them.

Parallel connection—sources of d.c. supply are connected in parallel when all terminals of like polarity are joined together.

ELECTRIC TRANSMISSION.
GENERATOR

A direct current ("d.c.") generator is employed with this form of transmission and it can be understood quite simply by reference to Fig. 69. The generator functions on the principle of electro-magnetic induction, i.e.—that when a conductor is moved across a magnetic field so that it breaks the lines of force, electro-motive force ("e.m.f.") is

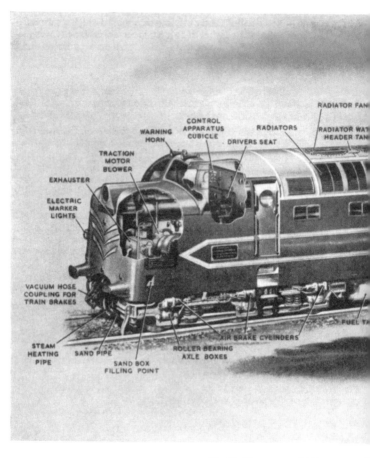

RADIATOR FAN

CONTROL
APPARATUS
CUBICLE

RADIATORS

WARNING
HORN

RADIATOR WAT
HEADER TAN

DRIVERS SEAT

TRACTION
MOTOR
BLOWER

EXHAUSTER

ELECTRIC
MARKER
LIGHTS

VACUUM HOSE
COUPLING FOR
TRAIN BRAKES

FUEL TA

AIR BRAKE CYLINDERS

STEAM
HEATING
PIPE

SAND PIPE

ROLLER BEARING
AXLE BOXES

SAND BOX
FILLING POINT

Fig. 68. The prototype 3,300-h.p. English

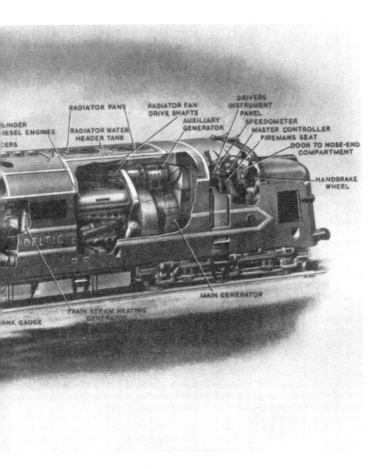

RADIATOR FANS

RADIATOR FAN
DRIVE SHAFTS

DRIVERS
INSTRUMENT
PANEL

LINDER
IESEL ENGINES

RADIATOR WATER
HEADER TANK

AUXILIARY
GENERATOR

SPEEDOMETER

MASTER CONTROLLER

ERS

FIREMANS SEAT

DOOR TO NOSE-END
COMPARTMENT

HANDBRAKE
WHEEL

DELTIC

MAIN GENERATOR

TRAIN STEAM HEATING
GENERATOR

ANK GAUGE

diesel-electric locomotive—equipment layout.

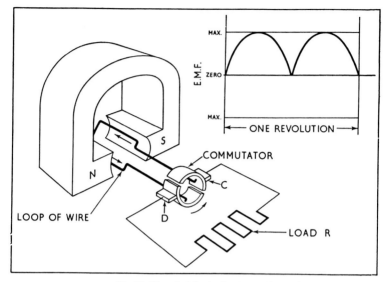

Fig. 69. The principle of a direct current generator.

induced within the conductor itself. The e.m.f. is measured in volts. If therefore, an open wire loop is made to rotate between the poles of a permanent magnet (N-S), e.m.f. will flow through the wire. Further reference to the illustration will reveal that the ends of the wire loop are connected to a split metal ring the two halves of which are insulated from each other. This ring, which rotates with the wire loop, is known as a commutator and the collecting brushes (C and D) ride upon it. The e.m.f. induced, varies during each revolution of the commutator, commencing at zero and rising to a peak, then falling to zero, during each half revolution as will be seen from the diagram. By increasing the number of wire loops (coils) the flow of current can be made very nearly constant but there must of course, be an increased number of segments in the commutator in proportion to the increased number of coils.

In practice the d.c. generator has many coils, consisting of insulated copper wire or strip and they are embedded in slots in a soft-iron laminated cylinder or core—the complete assembly being known as an armature. The permanent magnet shown in Fig. 69 is replaced by an electromagnet having many poles wound with insulated copper wire—termed "field coils" and the strength of the magnetic field which they produce ("excitation") depends on the number of turns of wire on each pole and the magnitude of the current in the coils.

Turning once more to Fig. 69, if the coil is closed by connecting the brushes (C and D) to an electrical resistance (R) electric current will flow through the loop and through the resistance itself—the latter representing the load imposed on the machine. The amount of current which flows is measured in amperes. When the wire loop is rotated in one direction current will flow in the particular segment under the south pole of the magnet (S) in the direction of the arrow and away from the brush (C) and then in the segment of wire under the north pole (N) and so towards the brush (D). From the brush (D) the current will pass along the wiring and back to brush (C) thus completing the circuit.

The output of the generator may be varied by altering the speed of rotation or by changing the magnetic strength of the "field" system. The former is obtained simply by varying the governor setting of the diesel engine to which the generator is coupled, and the latter by inserting variable resistances in the field system to vary the amount of current flowing through the coils of the electro-magnets. (*See page* 189).

The generator illustrated is self-ventilated by a fan which draws air through the unit to cool the windings and maintain them at safe working temperatures. The armature is supported at one end by the diesel engine flywheel and at the other by a roller-bearing housed in the end plate of the generator frame.

TRACTION MOTOR (*See Fig.* 70)

The traction motor is fundamentally similar to the generator already described and operates on the principle that if a coil, capable of being rotated in a magnetic field, is supplied through its commutator with direct current, the coil will rotate. Therefore, if the brushes (C and D in Fig. 69) were connected to the terminals of a battery instead of the load (R) the coil would rotate. The performance of this simple motor would be greatly increased if an iron core was inserted through the coil and additional coils introduced. An increased pole area and the provision of electro-magnets in place of the permanent one would further enhance the motor's performance.

For rail traction use the d.c. motor is usually of the series-wound type, which is to say that the current passing through the armature also passes through the field coils. A motor with this type of winding has a torque (turning force) proportional to the current flow multiplied by the magnetic strength of the field system and is capable therefore of producing high torque when the locomotive is started. In addition, this type of motor has an advantage in that as the load increases its speed drops.

The armature shaft of the traction motor is connected to the locomotive wheels by reduction gears and for hump shunting duties double-reduction gears are employed to enable a high motor speed to be used in spite of limitation to locomotive maximum speed (see Fig. 71). A traction motor blower is used to force cooling air through the traction motor and the air, taken from outside the locomotive to the blower, is usually filtered. Alternatively the air intake to the blower can be so arranged that virtually no dust is blown through the traction motors. In diesel-electric shunters the traction motor blower is mechanically driven by an extension shaft from the auxiliary generator, whilst on large locomotives it is usually duplicated and powered by electric motors supplied with current from the auxiliary generator.

The combination of an engine-driven generator and a series wound traction motor provides a basically sound means of converting the diesel's horsepower into the variable torque (turning power) and speed required at the locomotive wheels.

The inherent characteristics of this combination are such that when the generator is running at constant speed and supplying a traction motor, an increase of current demand produces a decrease in voltage,

Fig. 70. Axle-hung traction motor showing driving pinion.

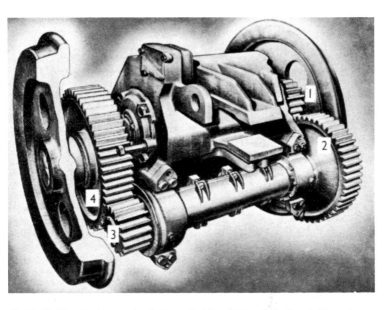

Fig. 71. Double-reduction gear for diesel-electric drive. I-2 First Reduction; 3-4 Second Reduction.

so that the power tends to remain constant. This characteristic contributes to the condition required whereby the locomotive's speed can vary while the engine speed and output remain constant.

Having examined very simply the electric generator and allied motor we will now investigate how these two units together with the diesel engine and undercarriage (or bogie) combine to provide diesel-electric power.

TRANSMISSION LAYOUT

In Fig. 72 the diesel-electric principle in its elementary form is illustrated. The diesel engine (A) rotates the armature (B) of the electric generator (represented by the magnet (C) and commutator (D) together with the armature (B)) and the current thus produced is conducted via the electric leads (E) to the traction motor armature (F). As the traction motor armature revolves it turns the drive shaft (G) and thus the spur gear (H), so driving the axle (I) and the wheels (J) through the medium of the axle gear (K).

It will be appreciated that Fig. 72 presents a diagrammatic scheme and many other considerations have to be taken into account—means of starting the diesel motor without running the locomotive for instance. It is necessary to store electrical energy to start the engine and to replenish this energy when it is drawn upon. If, however, the basic idea contained in the diagram is understood, the simplicity of electric transmission becomes apparent and it will be at once realised that no physical connections exist between the diesel motor-electric generator group and the traction motors, apart from wiring.

The shunting locomotive (Fig. 73) helps to illustrate the operation and robust simplicity of this form of transmission. The diesel engine (2) drives the electric generator (21), current from which is passed to the traction motors (18) in accordance with the driving controller position, and power is applied through the traction motor reduction gears (19) to the axles and wheels. It is usual for two traction motors to be employed one on the leading and the other on the trailing axles of a six-wheeled shunter. The intermediate coupled wheels are connected to the others by cranks and side rods as shown.

AUXILIARIES

A second and smaller generator is employed to provide electric current to the various motors operating the locomotive auxiliaries, e.g., compressor, exhauster, traction motor blower and the charging of the storage battery. This auxiliary generator is usually mounted on top of the main generator in the case of shunting locomotives and driven by multiple vee belts. On the larger locomotive engines the auxiliary generator is invariably overhung on the main generator, its armature being mounted on an extension of the main generator armature shaft.

Battery charging by the auxiliary generator is entirely automatic and commences as soon as the diesel engine is running and the auxiliary generator has built up the required voltage. When the voltage is correct a relay operates a contactor which closes and connects the auxiliary generator output to the battery terminals. Should current start to flow

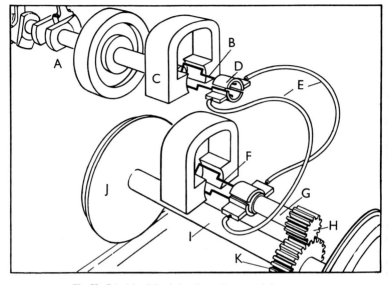

Fig. 72. Principle of diesel-electric traction transmission.

from the battery back to the generator armature a reverse current relay functions disconnecting the auxiliary generator from the storage battery. The battery, in addition to being used for starting the diesel engine, energises the field coils of the auxiliary generator and also supplies those electrical services required on the locomotive when the diesel engine is at a standstill (lighting circuits, control circuits and the fuel-supply motor).

HYDRAULIC TRANSMISSION

The fluid coupling described on page 96 represents one form of hydraulic transmission but of course, used only as a medium between diesel engine and gearbox. It is invariably filled with ordinary engine lubricating oil. The types of hydraulic transmission about to be described fulfil all the functions of speed-change mechanisms, some are true hydraulic drives whilst others employ mechanical clutches and are more accurately termed "hydro-mechanical" transmissions.

Torque converters require a cooling system for their hydraulic fluid and this is achieved by means of either a radiator or heat exchanger,

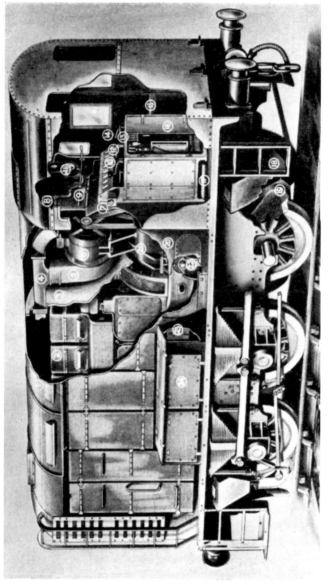

Fig. 73. English Electric 0-6-0 shunting locomotive.

1. Sliding roof; 2. Diesel Engine; 3. Bulkhead; 4. Air ducts; 5. Blower; 6. Auxiliary Generator; 7. Brake handle; 8. Light switches; 9. Sanding Valves; 10. Instrument Panel; 11. Speedometer; 12. Master Switch; 13. Reverser Handle; 14. Control Handle; 15. Driver's Seat; 16. Control Cubicle; 17. Deadman's Pedal; 18. Traction Motor; 19. Reduction Gear Casing; 20. Fuel Tank; 21. Generator; 22. Three-point suspension; 23. Battery Isolating

a typical layout being shown in Fig. 58 on page 88. In addition a pump must be included to keep the converter fully charged, any loss of fluid from the converter by any means whatsoever will lower its efficiency.

TORQUE CONVERTER PRINCIPLE.

Torque is the movement of a system of forces causing rotation. A fluid coupling (Fig. 75) is the simplest method of transmitting torque hydraulically and has a driving and driven member often called "impeller" and "turbine". The ratio of input to output torque never exceeds 1 to 1.

The principal difference between a fluid coupling and a torque converter is that the former simply transmits torque whilst the latter *multiplies* it. The characteristic of the fluid converter as distinct from a gearbox (which is a mechanical converter) is that the input torque and the speed remain constant at all rail speeds despite changes in output torque as output speed varies.

In order to make the fluid coupling perform as a torque converter it is only necessary to add the reaction member (see Fig. 76). The oil then circulates in the same manner as in the fluid coupling but while in the fluid coupling the blades are straight, the converter blading in all three elements is curved to guide the oil along the now more devious paths. The impeller rotated by the engine, pushes the oil outwards and against the turbine causing the turbine to turn. After striking the blades the oil is directed inwards towards the inner circumference of the turbine. As the oil leaves the turbine it is moving in a direction opposite to the impeller rotation and it is then directed against the reaction member which, being held stationary, causes the oil to change direction and add its energy to the impeller.

This redirected oil aids the impeller to rotate faster, adding to the input torque. The turbine does not, however, rotate as fast as the impeller and it is through this that the consequent output speed reduction is obtained. As the speed of the impeller further increases however, the turbine rotates faster until a point is reached when the torque demand diminishes and the relationship of the impeller to the turbine becomes 1 to 1, both rotating at the same speed.

Fig. 74 shows a section through a torque converter and the way in which power is transmitted through the unit. It should be noted that all moving parts rotate in a clockwise direction. The illustration shows a type of torque converter that has a free-wheeled reaction member and is described on pages 151 and 152.

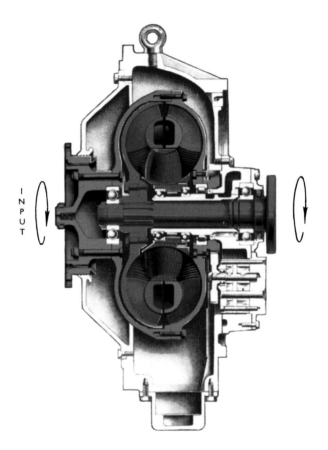

INPUT

Fig. 74. Section through torque converter.

114

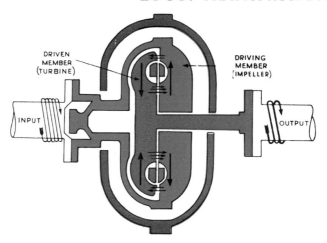

Fig. 75. Fluid coupling principle.

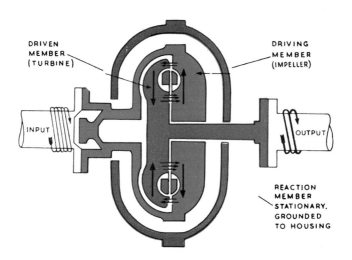

Fig. 76. Torque converter principle.

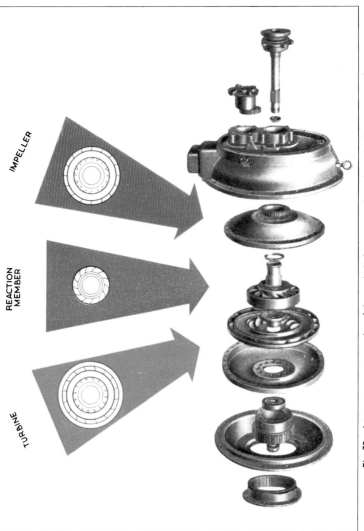

Fig. 77. A torque converter consists of three principal components housed together in a compact casing

Diesel engine idling, all circuits empty. Main pressure pump operating and energising oil supply lines to closed filling valve and first control valve.

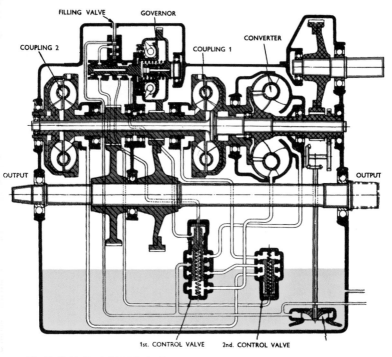

Fig. 78. Voith-North British hydraulic transmission-Stage I. (Colour Key on next page.)

● DRIVING PARTS   ● DRIVEN PARTS
● FIXED PARTS   ○ OIL

Diesel engine at steady operating speed. Filling valve open and governor passing oil to first control valve. Converter thereby filled and locomotive starting from rest. Nos. 2 and 3 circuits empty.

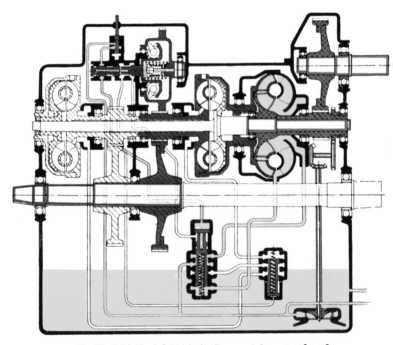

Fig. 79. Voith-North British hydraulic transmission system-Stage 2.

Diesel engine at steady operating speed. Locomotive in medium speed
nge. Governor actuating both control valves and keeping No. 2 circuit
led, Nos. 1 and 3 empty.

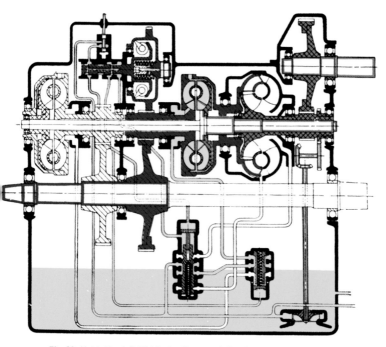

Fig. 80. Voith-North British hydraulic transmission-Stage 3.

● DRIVING PARTS ● DRIVEN PARTS
● FIXED PARTS ○ OIL

Diesel engine at steady operating speed and locomotive in high speed range. Governor actuating both control valves and keeping No. 3 circuit filled, Nos. 1 and 2 empty.

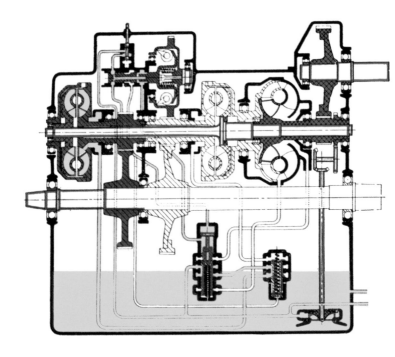

Fig. 81. Voith-North British hydraulic transmission-Stage 4.

--LOCO. TRANSMISSIONS

VOITH-NORTH BRITISH TRANSMISSION (*See Figs.* 78–81)

This system of hydraulic turbo transmission is now being used for line service locomotives on British Railways and consists of three fluid-circuits, first a torque converter for slow-speeds and starting from rest, followed by two fluid couplings, one of which is for intermediate and the other for high speed. The converter and fluid couplings are entirely self-contained and they are each brought into or out of action by filling or emptying the fluid.

The engagement of the three circuits is by means of an automatic governor which, dependent on locomotive speed, is supplied with oil by a pressure pump. At first the fluid is directed to the converter and then, as the locomotive speed rises, to No. 1 fluid coupling emptying the converter. As speed continues increasing at the rail the oil is fed by the governor to No. 2 fluid coupling automatically and empties coupling No. 1. The reverse action takes place as rail speed drops.

Usually this type of transmission is mounted as a separate unit to the diesel engine and the connection between the two is by means of a uni-versally-jointed shaft. The system is a straight hydraulic type without any mechanical clutches and the gear ratio between input and output shafts is determined by the converter and coupling engagements.

VOITH-N.B. CONVERTER

As illustrated the unit consists of an impeller or centrifugal pump, a turbine runner or driven member and a set of fixed blades. The pump, driven by the diesel engine, converts the engine power to kinetic energy (that is energy producing motion) in oil impinging on the turbine blades. The faster the pump blades move the less the relative impinging speed of the oil and the faster the locomotive moves through the action of the driven member. If the locomotive encounters increased resistance in driving upgrade the turbine or driven member slows down until the increased relative speed of the oil automatically increases the driving force to overcome the resistance.

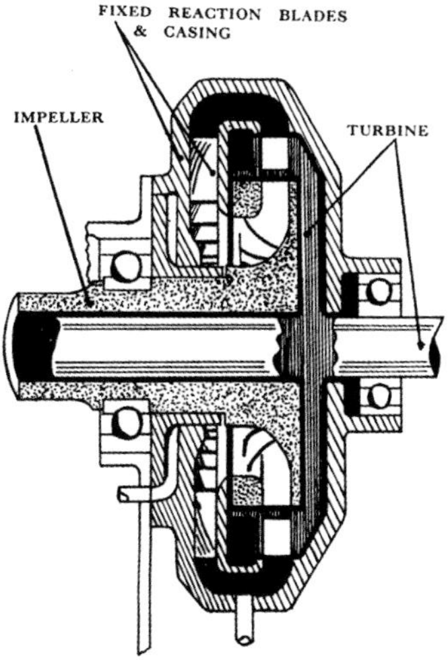

Fig. 82. Voith-North British torque converter.

121

The difference between output and input torque is taken by the fixed reaction blades which always guide the oil to the pump inlet in the most favourable direction, controlling the flow to the best advantage. Variations in speed and load at the turbine (output) do not effect the impeller (input) and the engine is thus protected against load changes and shocks.

Torque converter fluid action may be compared to a tap of running water beneath which is held a spoon. The force of the water presses the spoon down and at the same time the water splashes upwards. The force on the spoon comes from the fact that the water stream is *deflected*. In other words, the tap is the impeller, the water is the oil and the spoon is the blade on the turbine wheel. If you allow the spoon to move downwards at the same speed as the water than it will not deflect water and there will be no force on the spoon. However, as long as the spoon moves more slowly than the water a force is exerted. The force is maximum as long as the spoon is held rigidly and decreases the faster the spoon runs away from the water. Hence the engine can run at constant speed—which is that of the impeller (or water tap) whilst the turbine (or spoon) will vary in speed of rotation according to the speed of the locomotive which in turn is dependent on resistance at the rail.

VOITH-N.B. COUPLING

This unit follows in general standard fluid coupling practice except that, unlike the coupling shown in Fig. 62 on page 95, it is normally *empty* but can be filled with fluid at will from a fixed connection which is in the vicinity of the output shaft gland. When the coupling is engaged it is rapidly filled with oil and reaches a designed working range instantaneously and its function in the chain of events in the Voith-North British turbo transmission will now be described.

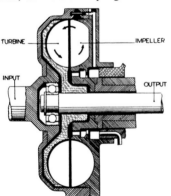

Fig. 83. Voith-North British coupling.

VOITH-N.B. CONTROL SYSTEM

The illustrations on pages 117–120 show the three-circuit transmission with one converter and two fluid couplings. The main factor in the control system is the governor, which is actuated from the output side—and therefore influenced by the speed at the rail, the diesel engine input being constant. The governor, according to the speed it runs, actuates the respective control valve, deciding which of the three circuits shall be supplied with oil. Only the chosen circuit is energised and that is the one which is most efficient or most suitable as regards road speed or track condition requirements.

The action is completely automatic and is dependent solely on the speed at the rail. As the locomotive gathers speed from rest (where the condition shown in stage 1 was realised) the governor ensures that at a predetermined road speed the first circuit, stage 2, which is always the converter, will empty and No. 2 circuit is engaged, stage 3. If the conditions are such that the locomotive continues to accelerate, No. 2 circuit is emptied and No. 3 brought into service, stage 4. Should resistance at the rail increase and speed fall the governor will ensure that the top speed circuit will be de-energised automatically and the medium speed circuit taken over again. This sequence of changing up and down can continue indefinitely, suiting the output of the transmission to the resistance at the rail without any move on the part of the driver. The emptying and filling of each fluid circuit is so arranged that the two adjacent circuits concerned with any particular change up or down are made to overlap and there is therefore no loss in momentum of train or drop in tractive effort (drawbar pull).

A single handwheel suffices for the main driver's control and this actuates the diesel engine throttle and the transmission filling valve. At idling speed the transmission is completely de-energised but movement of the control wheel in the cab increases the engine speed to the normal working r.p.m. and brings into operation the transmission, filling the first fluid-circuit as already described. The torque converter first engaged takes care of the high starting torque required to move the locomotive from rest, but from here onwards the transmission governor takes charge.

The sequence of operations shown is of course reversed as the locomotive decelerates.

MECHANICAL TRANSMISSION (*See Fig.* 84)

For small locomotives, such as 200-h.p. shunters, the straightforward mechanical transmission is usually employed and often the gearbox and final drive are combined in a single structure which invariably incorporates the reversing mechanism. The drawing illustrates a typical layout, the vertical diesel engine driving through a fluid coupling the S.C.G. gearbox and thence to the final drive, which is itself connected to the driving wheels by a jackshaft and coupling rods.

Fluid couplings used for locomotive installations are often of a more complicated pattern than the normal railcar or automotive type and sometimes employ the step-circuit principle (see page 97). A central reservoir is provided within the impeller unit and the effect of this form of coupling is to reduce drag torque when the engine is idling without increasing "slip" when working under load. Fusible plugs are provided as a precaution against overheating. This type of coupling is now beginning to make its appearance on higher horsepower railcar engines. Final drive units similar to the one shown on page 157 but with a further reduction stage through spur gears are installed and the "axle" shaft becomes a jackshaft with fly-cranks.

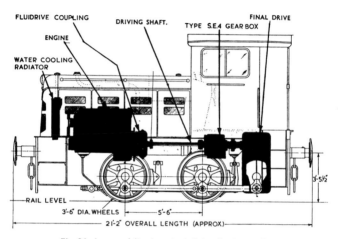

Fig. 84. Layout of diesel-mechanical shunting locomotive.

HYDRO-MECHANICAL TRANSMISSION (*See Fig.* 85)

The Stone-Maybach "Mekydro" transmission employed on Swindon-built locomotives was developed by Maybach Motorenbau of Germany —the company responsible for the engines described on pages 75–78. Although strictly speaking a hydraulic type, the "Mekydro" has been included under "hydro-mechanical" in view of the use of an integral change-speed gearbox.

A single torque converter together with four mechanically-selected speed changes is used so that the converter operates only within its best efficiency range. All the elements of the "Mekydro" transmission including the automatic control mechanism and the directional gear, are enclosed in a single oil-tight casing. The torque converter impeller (1) permanently filled with oil, is driven by the engine through a pair of step-up gears (2)

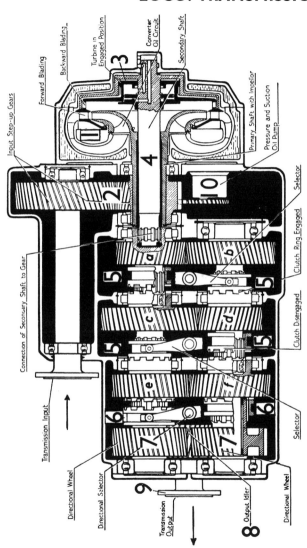

Fig. 85. Schematic sectioned view of the Stone-Maybach "Mekydro" hydro-mechanical transmission.

Forward Blading

Backward Blading

Turbine in Engaged Position

Converter Oil Circuit

Secondary Shaft

Input Step-up Gears

Primary Shaft with Impellor

Pressure and Suction Oil Pump

Connection of Secondary Shaft to Gear

Selector

Clutch Ring Engaged

Clutch Disengaged

Selector

Transmission Input

Directional Wheel

Directional Selector

Transmission Output

Output Idler

Directional Wheel

125

and a hollow shaft. The turbine wheel of the converter can be disengaged and functions as a disconnnectable coupling operated by means of a hydraulic cylinder.

The speed change gear train comprises three pairs of gears a–b, c–d, and e–f, appropriately coupled by clutches to give four gear ratios. The power-flow through the gear trains in the various ratios is shown on page 134. This speed change gear train is driven by the converter turbine via the splined shaft (4), which is located inside the hollow shaft of the input drive. The gear engagement clutches consist of two pairs of Maybach over-running dog clutches (5) which operate automatically in relation to the locomotive's speed and the engine load. A description and illustrations of these dog clutches is given on page 130.

Power is transmitted from the speed-change gear train to the directional gear train consisting of two gear wheels (7) in constant mesh with a common driven wheel (8) but not with each other. A further pair of clutches (6) engages one or other of the gears (7) according to the direction required and from the selected gear an output reduction gear train transmits the power to an output flange (9) which drives in turn the final drive on the axle by means of a propellor shaft.

A suction and pressure pump (10) driven from the input gear (2) supplies oil to the control mechanism, keeps the converter circuit filled and lubricates the transmission gears and bearings. Two heat exchangers are provided for oil cooling utilising the diesel engine cooling system, the main one cools the oil from the converter and a proportion of this oil is then further cooled in the second heat exchanger to supply the transmission lubrication and control circuits.

"MEKYDRO" CONTROL SYSTEM (*See Fig.* 86)

To operate the transmission after the engine has been started and the direction selector lever placed in the required position, the engine throttle controller must be moved to the first driving notch. The converter turbine (normally disengaged) is thereby engaged through the action of the electric solenoid (M3) and the locomotive begins to move.

All subsequent operations are carried out automatically, gear changes taking place as locomotive speed and engine load change. The two parts of the governor (R) driven by the primary and secondary sections of the torque converter (T) move the gear selector (A) through a selector valve by one notch into the next gear position. The gear selector feeds oil under pressure to the gear-change cylinder concerned (B or C) which in turn operates the appropriate selector for (N).

126

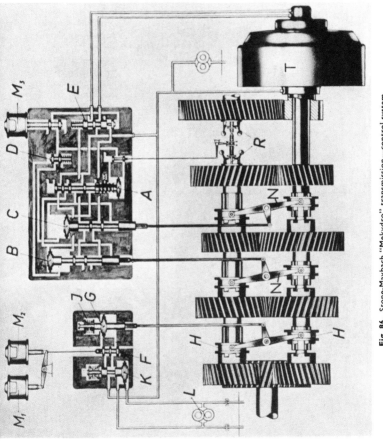

Fig. 86. Stone-Maybach "Mekydro" transmission—control system.

127

Cylinders (B and C) cannot disengage their dog clutches as long as the transmission is under load. To release the load, oil pressure is applied to cylinders (B) or (C) and at the same time operates the torque converter engagement valve (E) through the locking valve (D) so that the converter turbine takes up its disengaged position. The clutches are then disengaged and a light pressure is applied which will at a later stage engage the appropriate clutches for the next speed ratio.

By means of a control impulse produced by the piston of cylinder (B) or (C) in its intermediate valve position the forward turbine blading is engaged for a short while for an upward speed change and for a downward change the backward blading is engaged. The two halves of the dog clutch concerned are accelerated or decelerated until they synchronise and the over-running dog clutches engage. The control impulse is interrupted when the piston of (B) or (C) reaches its full travel and the converter resumes its working position, thus the speed change procedure which has taken only a fraction of a second, is completed. A delaying device in the control circuit prevents "hunting" between gears at any change-over point.

A direction selector lever is provided in the cab which through two electric solenoids (M1 and M2) actuates the valve (F). According to the position of the direction selector lever oil is fed under pressure to one side of the directional change cylinder piston, which moves the directional clutches (H) into one or other of their final positions. When the diesel engine is stopped oil pressure is cut off and the directional clutches are returned to the intermediate position by the action of spring (J) thus isolating the "Mekydro" unit from the driving axles. To prevent damage caused by a driver operating the direction selector lever before the locomotive has stopped, the directional safety valve (K) is always kept in the correct position (corresponding to the direction of motion) by the interlock oil pump (L) which is always in operation while the locomotive is moving thus preventing oil pressure from being applied to the wrong side of the directional change cylinder (G) until the locomotive comes to a stop.

Fig. 88 explains the features of dog clutches generally and the Maybach version in particular. Simple dog clutches like that shown in (1) enable disconnection of driving and driven shafts but engagement is only possible when both dogs are stationary. A conventional over-running dog clutch (2) allows automatic disengagement when the driven dog "b" begins to rotate faster than the driving dog "a".

With the Maybach design (3) the driving faces are unchanged from (1) but the inclined lateral faces of (2) have been included so as to permit positive engagement following any increase of speed of driving dog "a" relative to the speed of driven dog "b". The method of operation can now be followed by observing the right-hand illustrations starting at the top—if the driven dog rotates *faster* than the driving dog the inclined faces repel each other and engagement cannot take place (4). When the speed of the driven dog is decreased (or the speed of the driving dog

Fig. 87. British Railways diesel-hydraulic Type 3 locomotive with Mekydro transmission—see also pages 132-133.

increased) until both speeds match, the dogs rotate together but do not lock (5). From this condition of synchronisation any further change will cause the teeth of dog "a" to overtake the teeth of dog "b", a relative movement of from half to one tooth pitch immediately causing positive engagement (6).

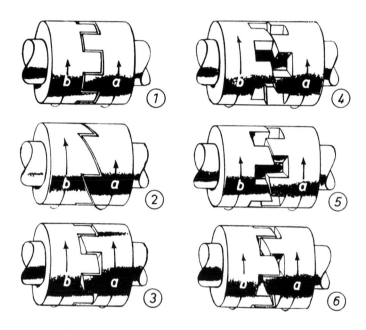

Fig. 88. Stone-Maybach "Mekydro" transmission—Dog clutch.

DIESEL-HYDRAULIC LOCO. (*See Fig.* 89)

Type 3 British Railways' locomotives operating in the Western Region and produced by Beyer Peacock (Hymek) Limited are fitted with a single Maybach MD870 diesel engine, pressure charged and inter-cooled and rated at 1,700 b.h.p. at 1,500 r.p.m.

As will be seen from the drawings overleaf, the engine (1) is coupled by a short carden shaft to the Mekydro transmission unit (2) which is of type K184 U.

130

LOCO. TRANSMISSIONS

From the transmission unit propeller shafts connect to the final drive gearboxes located on the inner axle of each bogie. A further carden shaft on each bogie connects to the final drive gearboxes on the outer axles.

Pneumatic control is used for the speed of the diesel engine but all other control functions are taken care of electrically. The main items of control equipment are located in a dust-proof cabinet (27) contained in the "A" End cab.

Starting is carried out by means of a dynostarter which is coupled to the transmission on the input side of the torque converter by a suitable propeller shaft. This unit turns the engine to start it and when the diesel is running generates current for battery charging and auxiliary unit operation.

Cooling of the engine and transmission is arranged by a Serck-Behr self-contained unit (see page 82) and incorporates header tanks fitted with a hydraulically driven fan. The radiator shutters and fan speed are of course thermostatically controlled.

An interesting feature is the preheating of the engine cooling system by means of an oil-fired preheater unit (5) which is intended to minimise the rapid wear normally occurring immediately after starting an engine from cold.

The undercarriage is mounted on two cast-steel bogies of "Commonwealth" design incorporating swing bolsters, triple-elliptic nests of springs between equaliser beams and bogie frame, and laminated springs below the bolster.

The locomotive braking is of the compressed air type with vacuum braking for the train, the locomotive's brakes being controlled by the vacuum-brake valve or independently by the straight air-brake valve.

One compressor and two Northey exhausters are fitted and compressed-air sanding gear operated by pedal controlled electro-pneumatic valves is employed. The cab front windows are glazed with electrically-heated "Therglas".

Among the protective equipment installed may be mentioned diesel engine and locomotive overspeed, engine oil pressure, cooling water temperature and transmission oil temperature as well as water level in radiator header tanks.

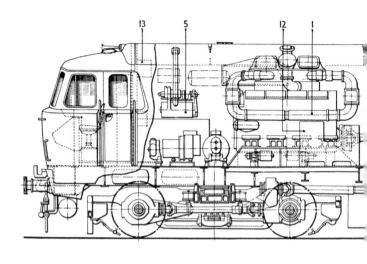

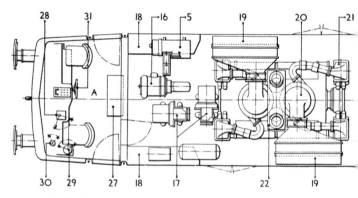

1. Diesel engine.	9. Dynostarter.
2. Transmission.	10. Hydraulic pump (fan drive).
3. Cooling group.	11. Hydraulic motor (fan drive).
4. Train-heating boiler.	12. Engine instrument panel.
5. Engine preheater.	13. Automatic voltage regulator.
6. Water tanks.	14. Final drive gearboxes.
7. Main fuel tanks.	15. A.W.S. shoe.
8. Reserve fuel tank.	16. Air compressor.

Fig. 89. Layout of Hymek diesel-hy

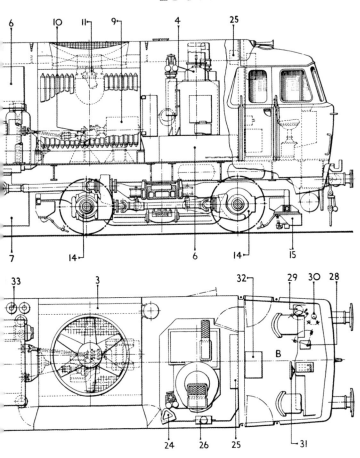

17. Exhausters.	25. Toilet water tank.
18. Batteries.	26. Boiler water tank.
19. Air intake filters.	27. Control cubicle.
20. Pressure-chargers.	28. Controller.
21. Intercoolers.	29. Vacuum brake valve.
22. Exhaust silencer.	30. Air brake valve.
23. Transmission heat exchanger.	31. Hand brake.
24. Toilet.	32. Shore supply unit.
	33. Fire extinguisher bottles.

b.h.p. locomotive. (British Railways)

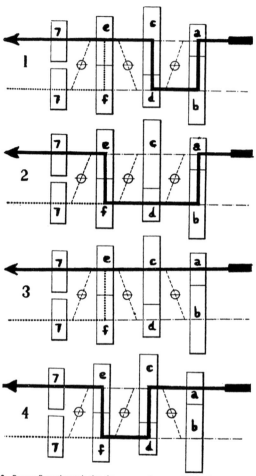

Fig. 90. Power flow through the change-speed gears of Mekydro transmission.

1st GEAR—Double reduction (ratio 1:2.7).
2nd GEAR—Single reduction (ratio 1:1.6).
3rd GEAR—Direct Drive (ratio 1:1).
4th GEAR—Over Drive (ratio 1.7:1).

(In the reverse direction of rotation the power flow is indicated by the dotted line.)

CHAPTER TEN

THE TRANSMISSION SYSTEM

RAILCARS

As WITH THE diesel locomotive where there is the choice of several transmission systems, so with the diesel railcar, but whereas electric transmission
is favoured for locomotives in Britain today, mechanical drive is predomi-
nant for railcars. Railcar transmissions are usually of the mechanical,
hydro-mechanical or electric types. At the time of writing there are over
3,000 railcars at work on British Railways, of which about 2,000 are
power-cars. There are a number of diesel-electric cars in service on the
London-Tunbridge Wells-Hastings route and in the Hampshire area. As
far as electric railcar transmissions are concerned they follow the principles
already established in Chapter 9, and the S.R. trains consist of two motor
coaches with four trailers between them making a basic six-car set for
the longer routes. Each motor coach is fitted with an English Electric
4SRKT pressure-charged four-cylinder diesel coupled to a main generator
from which current is supplied to two axle-hung traction motors carried
on the *rear* bogie of the motor coach. In this way there are but two powered
bogies in the six-car train with a total of four traction motors, which, by
the way, are identical to and interchangeable with those used on the latest
S.R. electric stock.

RAILCAR MECHANICAL TRANSMISSION (*See Fig.* 91)

Most mechanical drive railcars operating in Britain today employ two
four-wheel bogies, the inner axles of which are driven. Two engines are
provided and mounted beneath the floor of the railcar, each engine driving
its adjacent bogie through the medium of a fluid coupling (Fig. 62), a short
propeller shaft incorporating a freewheel (Fig. 65), a gearbox (Fig. 103),
followed by a longer propeller shaft and a final drive unit mounted on the
axle. Each diesel-mechanical railcar therefore has two engines, two fluid
couplings, four propeller shafts, two gearboxes and two final drives. We
have already dealt in some detail with fluid couplings and freewheels
in Chapter Eight—the remaining units are the gearbox and final drive.

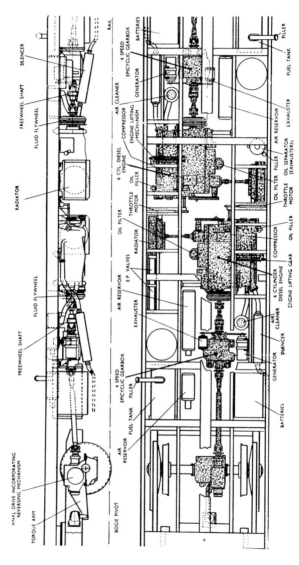

Fig. 91. Diesel-mechanical railcar—location of traction units.

136

RAILCAR TRANSMISSIONS

SELF-CHANGE GEARBOX

One of the features of British railcar and multiple-unit train development has been the use of the self-changing gearbox, initially in its manually operated form and, more recently, air-operated with control by means of electro-pneumatic valves. Invariably this gearbox is used in conjunction with a fluid coupling.

The S.C. gear was the brain child of the late Major W. G. Wilson, a motoring pioneer from the 1890s, hence the term "Wilson Gearbox", and the first application of his epicyclic gear was in the form of a 1914 tank steering mechanism.

The problem solved by this gearbox was that of engaging without "crashing" two or more gear wheels revolving independently and at different speeds. This was overcome by eliminating altogether the need to actually *engage* gears. Briefly, the s.c. gearbox mechanism may be divided into three sections: (i) the gearing, (ii) the band brake and (iii) the brake operating device. Let us deal with each in turn.

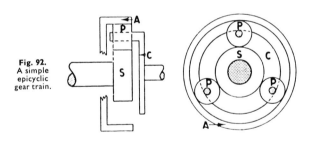

Fig. 92.
A simple
epicyclic
gear train.

THE GEARING

The gearing consists of a number of gear "trains", each train comprising three elements which revolve about a common centre. These three components are known as the Sunwheel, the Carrier and the Annulus (the latter being an internally toothed gear) items S, C and A respectively in Fig. 92. Meshing between the teeth of the annulus and the teeth of the sunwheel and mounted on the carrier are the idler gears, usually termed "planet" gears—P in Fig. 92, and reference to this diagram will show quite clearly how all the gears in any one "train" are in constant mesh.

137

The number of planet gears illustrated is three although other combinations are found. By connecting one or more of the elements of one "train" with those of similar "trains", various gear ratios are obtained—this being the principle employed in the self-changing gearbox. (*See pages* 175 *to* 177).

THE BAND BRAKE

A band brake consists of two concentric bands the friction linings of which are situated side by side. They are self-wrapping brakes, i.e. the friction of the brakes on the brake drums tends to increase their grip. The outer band, when constricted by the action of the brake operating mechanism, closes the inner band and both linings are thus brought into contact with the drum. The linings are of material which is extremely hard wearing and is suitable for working immersed in oil. The brakes are centralised about the drums in such a manner as to prevent them rubbing when in "off" position.

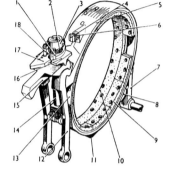

Fig. 93. A single band brake removed from the gearbox.

1. Adjuster Platform Spring Pin.
2. Adjuster Spring.
3. Adjuster Nut.
4. Adjusting Screw.
5. External Brake Band.
6. Adjusting Screw Locknut.
7. Internal Brake Band Link.
8. Centraliser Lug.
9. Internal Brake Band Lining.
10. External Brake Band Lining.
11. Centraliser Lug.
12. Brake Band Hook.
13. Internal Brake Band.
14. Brake Band Pull Rod.
15. Thrust Pad.
16. Adjuster Platform.
17. Adjuster Ring.
18. Adjuster Ring Spring Pin.

BRAKE OPERATING MECHANISM (*See Fig.* 94)

The means employed to apply the individual band brakes and release them as required is shown in this illustration and it should be noted that not more than one brake is "ON" at any one time. First, it will be observed

138

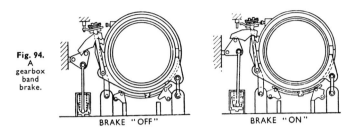

Fig. 94.
A gearbox band brake.

BRAKE "OFF"   BRAKE "ON"

that one end of each band brake is firmly anchored to the gearbox casing, while the other end is free. Now, when a gear change is made, the free end of the band brake concerned is pulled towards the fixed end and held there so that the brake grips and holds stationary the annulus with which it is mated. This operation on most railcars and locomotives is by air cylinders equipped with pistons and operated by the compressed-air supply available on rail traction units. It is obvious that, as the band brake friction lining wears, provision must be made to counteract this. This is achieved by the action of an ingenious little mechanism called the automatic adjuster (Fig. 95) and as the linings wear, the fixed and free ends of the band brakes are automatically brought gradually closer together, thereby compensating for wear on the brake linings. The automatic adjuster ring (4) striking the adjuster screw (1) is rotated anti-clockwise and, as the ring is pinned to the spring (3) in such a way this action

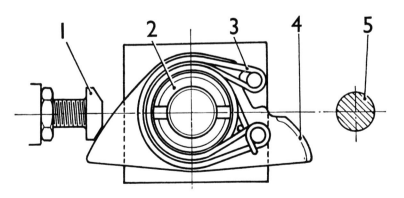

Fig. 95. Gearbox automatic adjuster.

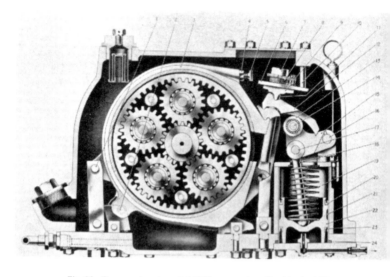

Fig. 96. Cross-section through Self-Change gearbox (Band-brake OFF).

Fig. 97. Cross-section through Self-Change gearbox (Band-Brake ON).

140

loosens the spring from contact with the adjuster nut (2). When the whole assembly moves to the "off" position (i.e. away from the screw) the rear portion of the ring strikes the tail pin (5) and rotates in a clockwise direction, taking with it the nut, which is consequently screwed down, taking up movement created by lining wear. By comparing Figs. 96 and 97 the amount of movement of the band brake operating mechanism may be judged—for first speed in this istance—and the linkage between the air piston and the band brake itself can be clearly seen.

OPERATION

Let us now consider the method of making the gear "trains" transmit the drive from the engine to the axle. How this is achieved is shown in the illustration Fig. 98, here the simple gear depicted in Fig. 92 has the drive from the engine connected to the input shaft S.1, which is in one with the sunwheel S. The mechanism being driven is connected to the output shaft S.2 which is integral with the carrier C, and finally the annulus A is held stationary by the band brake B.

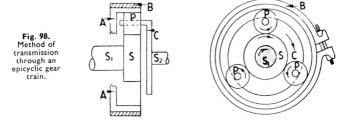

Fig. 98. Method of transmission through an epicyclic gear train.

The drive from the engine will cause the sunwheel S to turn and, since the planet wheels P are engaged with the sunwheel S, they too will turn. However, as the planet wheels are also engaged with the annulus which is held stationary by the brake, they roll around the inside of the annulus taking with them the planet carrier C and the shaft S.2. In this way the drive from the engine is transferred to the axle. The arrows in the diagram indicate the rotation of the direction of the various parts.

It should now be clear that, if a number of gear "trains" are connected together and a band brake is provided for each "train", then each time a brake is applied a gear change is made *with the gears always in mesh*. Reference should now be made to pages 174–176 where 1st, 2nd and 3rd speed engagements are illustrated in colour. The exception to this rule is that when a change into top gear is made, none of the band brakes is applied, but instead a plate clutch is engaged which gives a direct drive from the engine to the propeller shaft.

RAILCAR GEARBOX (*See Fig.* 99)

The unit illustrated is fitted to British Railways 300 h.p. railcars. From the part-sectioned view of this gearbox the assembly of the various components may be followed and looking along the main shaft from left to right in the centre are the direct-drive top speed clutch with its multi-plate assembly (A), following which are the third, second (B) and first speeds. Below this running gear can be seen the brake cylinder block (N) containing three air cylinders employed for band brake operation of the three indirect speeds.

The pistons are of varying size according to the load required from each brake. "Vee" belt pulleys are provided on the input and output couplings and these are used to drive an exhauster and generator.

A sectioned view of the top speed clutch operating piston, cylinder and linkage is shown at lower left. The multi-plate clutch operates so as to lock together the two running gear elements and, by preventing rotation of the gear trains *relative to each other*, causes all the gearing to rotate as one unit thus providing a direct drive from the input shaft (C) to the output shaft (D). From Fig. 103 it will be seen that air is admitted to the bottom of the top speed operating cylinder forcing the piston upwards and with it the piston rod, which in turn is linked to a lever pivoted on a pin. Acting on a trunnion ring, this lever converts the pressure of the piston into movement parallel to the input shaft and thus applies the clutch.

Admission of air at a pressure of approximately 60–65 lbs. per square inch, to each of the gearbox cylinders is by the medium of electrically controlled air-valves influenced by the electric gear change controller in the driving compartment.

Lubrication of the gearbox is provided for by means of a gear type oil pump mounted on the front casing of the gearbox and the oil, under pressure, passes through an external feed pipe to an oil "muff" fitted on the output shaft from whence it is delivered to the gear trains and bearings. A lubricating oil filter of the paper-element type is also provided.

The combination of a self-change gearbox and a fluid coupling provides a highly efficient means of transmission and the operation of a number of gearboxes from one control is simple. The driver moves his gear controller to the desired position and thus energises the e.p.v. appropriate to this gear. The e.p. valve permits the air to act on the piston for the particular gear, the piston applies the band brake and the desired gear is obtained.

RAILCAR HYDRO-MECHANICAL TRANSMISSION

At the time of writing there are several railcars in service on British Railways with hydro-mechanical transmissions and 16 of these use the

Fig. 99. Part-sectioned view of railcar gearbox.

A. Direct Drive Clutch; B. Second Gear Train; C. Input Coupling; D. Output Coupling; E. Oil Filter; F. Flexible Oil Pipe; G. External Band; H. Internal Band; I. Mounting Bracket; J. V-belt Grooves; K. Oil Pump Gear; L. Top Speed Cylinder; M. Third Speed Piston; N. Brake Cylinder Block; O. Air Union; P. Automatic Adjuster.

Lysholm-Smith type produced by the Leyland side of B.U.T., Ltd. A. considerable number of cars are fitted with Lysholm-Smith three-stage converters to a design by Twin-Disc of America but produced under licence by Rolls-Royce. Two railcars are in service with both converters and gearboxes and as the torque-converters are of the Schneider-S.C.G. type there also are described and illustrated.

TWIN-DISC ROLLS-ROYCE CONVERTER (*See Figs.* 100–102)

The "DF" type converter used with Rolls-Royce engined cars is illustrated on the opposite page and is of the three-stage type, so called because the driven-member (or turbine) employs three separate sets of vanes (B1, B2 and B3), each receiving streams of fluid in turn. By this means a torque multiplication as high as 5.3 times the input from the engine can be achieved. The three basic parts of this converter are the impeller (A), which is driven by the engine and has only on ring of blades; the turbine made up of the three sets of blades already mentioned and connected to the output shaft (on the right of the illustration), and the reaction or guide vanes mounted in two rings (C1 and C2) attached to the stationary casing.

When the input shaft is driven, the impeller blades (A) force the fluid outwards, striking first the ring of turbine blades (B1). The fluid having changed direction to give initial torque to the turbine, is then re-directed to the first set of guide vanes (C1) to impinge on the second set of turbine blades (B2), adding more torque to the turbine. Similarly, the fluid is redirected by the second set of guide vanes (C2), to the third set of turbine blades (B3).

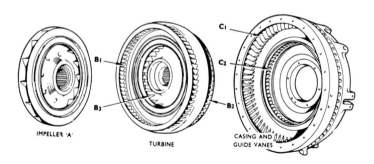

Fig. 100. Exploded view of Twin-Disc converter.

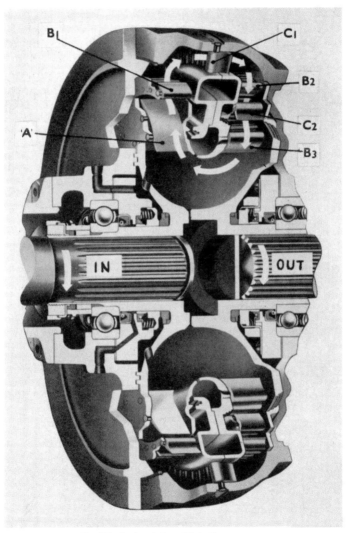

Fig. 101. Sectioned view of Twin-Disc converter.

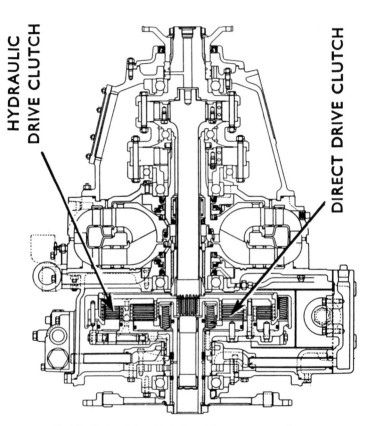

HYDRAULIC DRIVE CLUTCH

DIRECT DRIVE CLUTCH

Fig. 102. Sectioned view of Rolls-Royce DFR converter assembly.

146

Under operating conditions, when the output speed is approaching the maximum, the fluid passes quickly aroudd the circuit, striking each blade at only a small angle to the normal. As the load on the output shaft increases the turbine slows down, the striking angle is increased and the output torque rises.

The converter works in conjunction with a hydraulically-operated multi-plate frcition clutch which is automatically brought into engagement when the input and output torque are equal and at this point the transmission functions on a purely *mechanical* basis. In this way it will be seen that the unit does away with gear changing completely. Fig. 102 clearly shows the direct drive clutch and also the hydraulic drive clutch used with the converter unit.

To the right of the converter in Fig. 102 will be seen two small assemblies and these are the freewheel units. The turbine of the converter has a freewheel (or "one-way clutch") which allows the turbine to drive the output shaft in hydraulic-drive only—thus during periods of direct-drive it prevents the output shaft wasting energy by driving the idle turbine.

The additional freewheel is on the direct-drive output shaft and permits coasting of the train thus saving fuel and without overspeeding the engine. It also prevents the driving wheels becoming locked through an engine seizure.

Twin-Disc units are installed together with Rolls-Royce engines in the motor cars of trains operating in the Eastern Region, the London Midland Region St. Pancras–Bedford services and certain single-engined railcars on South Lancashire routes.

U.T.A. RAILCAR TRANSMISSION

A variation on the hydro-mechanical transmission theme is employed on the Ulster Transport Authority's diesel cars. These particular units are capable of being used as passenger trains or light goods locomotives and may be worked in multiple as required under the control of one driver.

The general layout of the power-transmission group is as follows:— a single B.U.T.-Leyland 900 series diesel (Fig. 47) is used which is turbocharged to 275 b.h.p. and provides the power which is transmitted through an S.C.G.-Schneider torque converter (Page 148) and thence via a freewheel-shaft (Fig. 65) to a bi-directional gearbox of the epicyclic type (page 159). From the bi-directional box the drive is taken by propeller shafts to an S.C.G. gearbox having four speeds and finally to an inner and outer final drive (Fig. 111) mounted on the respective axles of the appropriate bogie.

From this brief description it will be seen that both axles of the same bogie are driven. Speed changes are automatic by means of the Self-Changing Gears voltage sensitive control system.

SCHNEIDER-S.C.G. CONVERTER (*See Fig.* 103)

This is a single-stage type converter, which is usually unit-mounted on the engine. The main components are the impeller or pump (4), the turbine (1) and the reaction member (5). All these are single-piece aluminium castings with blades or vanes directing the flow of oil as already described for other single-stage units. Engine power is transmitted from the impeller to the turbine which is connected to the output shaft. An interesting feature, however, is that the reaction member (5) which, it will be observed, is placed between the impeller and turbine, is mounted on a freewheel (the rollers of which may be seen in the illustration) which allows it to take the reaction in the normal way of a static unit but also to move with the other two members when the coupling-point is reached. The converter is kept filled with oil under pressure by an oil pump. The oil pump is mounted on the side wall of the converter housing.

This unit in effect combines a hydraulic torque converter and a fluid flywheel into a single unit whilst retaining the advantages of each. Transfer from the converter range to the flywheel range is effected automatically. Engine power is transmitted through the input shaft (3) and pump cover (2) to the pump (4). The turbine (1) mounted opposite the pump is, by means of a splined hub, attached to the output shaft (6). The reaction member (5) is mounted between the pump and the turbine and it receives oil after it leaves the turbine and re-directs it into the pump. The function of the reaction member is to increase torque in the converter range.

This type of converter is employed on B.U.T. single engined railcars of multi-purpose design in service with U.T.A. The Schneider unit is used, together with a conventional self-change gearbox but with the addition of a bi-directional gearbox of the epicyclic type mounted between the converter and the self-change box. This unit enables the reversing mechanism to be disassociated from the design of the final drives, but it will be appreciated that the self-change gearbox has to be capable of operation in both directions of rotation.

The single-engined U.T.A. cars to which this form of hydro-mechanical transmission is fitted are capable of being used either as passenger units or light goods locomotives. Two British Railways cars have been fitted with similar transmissions but using reversing type final drives. The Ulster cars drive both axles of a single bogie whilst the B.R. units drive a single axle of each bogie.

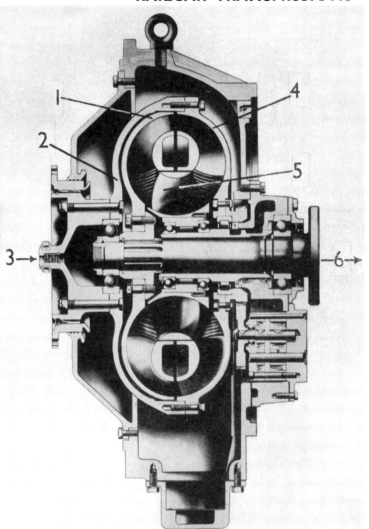

Fig. 103. Schneider System Converter produced by Self-Changing Gears Ltd.
(A colour illustration of this unit is shown in Fig. 74.)

149

Fig. 104. Lysholm-Smith torque converter components.

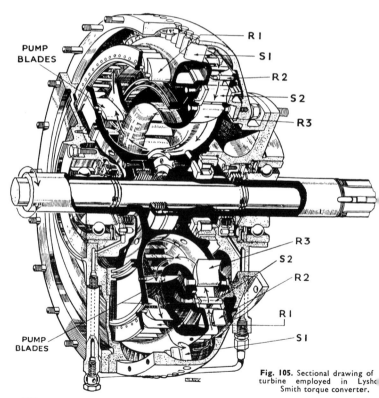

Fig. 105. Sectional drawing of turbine employed in Lysholm-Smith torque converter.

RAILCAR TRANSMISSIONS

LYSHOLM-SMITH CONVERTER (*See Fig.* 105)

The converter illustrated is of the Lysholm-Smith type and its function is to multiply the engine torque in much the same way as it is multiplied by the gearing of the conventional gearbox. Two plate-type clutches are mounted directly on the engine flywheel, that nearest the engine (A in Fig. 104) is mounted on a shaft passing through the centre of the converter, thus providing a direct drive. The second clutch (B in Fig. 104) provides the drive to the converter proper and is fitted on a hollow shaft, the other end of which is connected to the turbine unit (Fig. 105) inside the converter casing.

The two clutches are used as *couplings only.* They do not take up the drive as in a conventional clutch and are, therefore, subject to little wear. Though not strictly necessary, an intermediate or neutral position is provided, in which both clutches are disengaged. This allows for starting and testing the engines. The torque converter itself (Fig. 105) consists of a centrifugal pump mounted in a single casing with a three-stage hydraulic turbine. The pump wheel which is coupled to the engine flywheel by means of the clutch already mentioned, is similar in form to the impeller of an engine water-circulating pump. The turbine, which is connected to the propeller shaft through a flywheel, consists of a bladed rotor on which three separate rows of blades (R1, R2 and R3) are fixed in such a position that they are divided by two rings of *stationary* blades (S1 and S2) fixed to the stator or casing.

The casing is filled with fluid so that when power from the engine is transmitted to the pump, the fluid is driven from the pump on to the first set of rotor blades (R1), then through the stationary baldes (S1) where its flow is redirected on to the second set of rotating blades (R2), through the stationary blades (S2), where its direction is again changed on to the third set of rotor blades (R3) and so back to the pump. Owing to the shape of the blading and the fact that the fluid impinges on three sets of blades coupled in series, the engine torque is multiplied up to a ratio of approximately 5 to 1.

Seals as shown in Fig. 63 (R) on page 96 are used to prevent short-circuiting of fluid between the rotor and casing and other seals are provided to prevent loss of fluid. Slight leakage through these seals is, however, encouraged for the purpose of lubrication and this fluid is collected in a small sump, being automatically returned to the reserve tank of the system by an ejector.

A freewheel is provided on the shaft driven by the turbine rotor and this *converter* freewheel enables the torque converter to be completely isolated and to come to rest immediately a change to direct drive is made. In addition, the direct-drive shaft from the first friction-clutch is provided with its own freewheel.

FINAL DRIVES

A final drive and reverse gearbox of B.U.T. type, as fitted to B.R. diesel cars, is shown in Fig. 106 and it will be observed from the photograph Fig. 109 that it is mounted (by means of ball and roller bearings) directly on the driving axle between the wheels. The unit is held in position radially by the torque-arm (A), which is secured to the bogie frame through rubber mountings at the point (J). Laterally the whole axle assembly is located by the axle boxes in the bogie horns. The propeller shaft from the self-change gearbox connects with the coupling flange (B), which rotates the splined shaft (Fig. 106-B) on which rides the sliding dog (F). The sliding dog is under the influence of the compressed-air reversing mechanism, which is shown in Fig. 106 in its neutral position. Until the sliding dog is moved one way or the other by the reversing mechanism the splined shaft will rotate idly with no effect on the driving axle.

Contained within the forward-reverse mechanism are two air pistons connected by a rod from which is suspended a striking-fork which engages with the sliding dog. This assembly can be moved in either direction as compressed air is admitted to either of the cylinders. When air is applied the striking-fork moves with the piston rod and takes with it the sliding dog, the teeth of which engage with either the forward or reverse pinions seen in Fig. 107. Motion is conveyed from the pinion Fig 108 (5) to the bevel wheel (6), this is the first or primary gear reduction and motion is then conveyed to the straight spur wheel (7) and so to the axle spur gear to effect a secondary reduction. It will be seen, therefore, that a double-reduction gearing is employed and in actual practice this is 2.81 to 1 (2.81 turns of the propeller shaft to achieve one turn of the driving wheels). In top gear—which is a direct drive through the gearbox—the ratio is therefore the same and 2.81 turns of the engine crankshaft are required to turn the driving wheels one revolution.

The forward and reverse mechanisms of both the final drives of a railcar are controlled simultaneously by a lever in the driving compartment which operates electro-pneumatic valves, allowing air to be applied to one or other of the pistons. In emergencies it is possible to place any one of the final drive units of a railcar or multiple-unit train into the positive neutral (non-driving) position by means of the hand-operated plunger (Fig. 109-K). When turned a quarter circle this plunger engages with the reversing mechanism when the selector is moved, so locking it in the middle position. The final drive casing has the axle passing through it and as it contains lubricating oil, glands are provided at the points where the axle emerges.

152

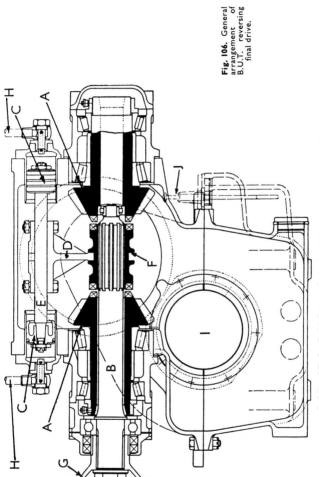

Fig. 106. General arrangement of B.U.T. reversing final drive.

A. Bevel Pinion; B. Splined Shaft; C. Air Piston; D. Striking Fork; E. Piston Rod; F. Sliding Dog; G. Prop. Shaft Coupling Flange; H. Air Pipe; I. Axle; J. Oil Level Dipstick.

PRIMARY BEVEL PINION

ENGAGEMENT DOG STRIKING FORK.

ENGAGEMENT DOG

REVERSE BEVEL PINION.

DRIVING SHAFT.

Fig. 107. Close-up view of reversing-drive mechanism.

154

Fig. 108.
Final Drive
Components.
2. Splined Drive Shaft.
3. Sliding Dog.
4. Coupling Flange.
5. Bevel Pinion.
6. Bevel Wheel.
7. Spur Gear.

Fig. 109.
(below)

Final Drive
Unit with
axle and
wheels.
A. Torque Arm.
B. Coupling Flange.
C. Air Cylinder.
D. Bevel Pinion.
E. Axle.
I. Casing.
J. Pivot point.
K. Neutral Plunger.
L. Bevel Housing Cap.

155

Fig. 110. Vertical Section of RF.28 Final Drive.

A. Selector Fork.   C. Top Shaft.   D. Axle.
E. Driving Pinion.   F. Bevel Wheel.   G. Indicator Switch.

With the advent of more powerful railcar engines other types of final drives were used and illustrated is type RF28 produced by Self-Changing Gears, Ltd. and fitted to cars having Rolls-Royce and B.U.T. engines around 230 bhp.

The principle of double-reduction, first through the bevel assembly and then through straight spur gears is again used but the reversing mechanism is mounted at right angles to the car and this drive and its components are of very robust construction to withstand the higher torque figures encountered with the more powerful prime movers.

156

From Fig 110 it will be seen that the spiral bevel pinion (E) is meshed with two bevel wheels—one of which is shown (F). The bevel wheels are free on the top shaft (C) the centre portion of which is splined to carry the sliding dog which is engaged with either one or other of the bevel wheels depending on the direction of drive selected. The dog is moved by means of the selector fork (A) influenced by the usual arrangement of air cylinders and pistons. Note the robust fork which is fitted with renewable rubbing pads. One of the straight spur gears may be seen in the illustration mounted on the axle (D) whilst a direction indicator switch (G) is incorporated to ensure positive indication that the dog clutch is fully engaged.

The RF28 unit is pressure lubricated by a pump located in the base of the casing and gear-driven from the axle, the oil being pumped to a distribution pipe in the top of the drive from whence oil jets feed the bevel gears whilst the bearings are fed by means of oil-ways. This particular type of reversing final drive is extensively used on shunting locomotives of around 200 bhp.

Fig. III. RF.28 Final Drive mounted on axle.

A. Input Coupling. B. Direction Indicator Switch. C. Air Cylinder.
D. Oil Filler. E. Drain Plug. F. Oil Feed Pipe.

SEPARATE REVERSERS

In the case of the final drive units just described a reversing mechanism was incorporated in the design. There are, however, several railcar applications where the reversing unit is a complete assembly on its own.

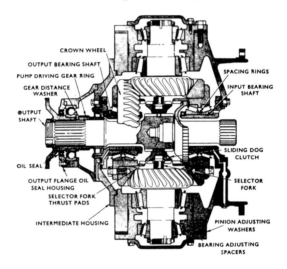

Fig. 112. Rolls-Royce CG 100 Reverser Unit.

The Rolls-Royce CG.100 unit gives a positive and continuous drive in either direction and is usually mounted directly to the rear of the torque converter thereby completing a compact diesel-hydraulic power unit.

The drive is transmitted through two spiral bevel gears which as will be seen from Fig. 112 are in constant mesh with two pinions. All gears are carried on taper-rolling bearings. Direction of drive is obtained by a sliding dog clutch operated by a selector fork which in turn is controlled by a three-position air cylinder (not illustrated) under the influence of the cab control. Movement of the selector fork is limited by adjustable stops. The splines on which the dog-clutch slides are thinner at the ends than in the middle thus preventing the clutch from working out of mesh under load.

A toggle device inside the unit prevents the dog-clutch from "dwelling" in the neutral position, ensures rapid re-engagement and eliminates speeding-up of the bevel gears and resultant damage to drive teeth when a change of direction is made. The reverser can, however, be pinned in Neutral by means of a hand control lever or by the application of air to both sides of the three position cylinder. The local hand control lever on the unit also enables the reverser to be locked in Forward or Reverse if required.

We have already dealt with the principles of the epicyclic gear and detailed its employment in railcar change-speed gearboxes. A further use of this system is found in the RRE1 unit which incorporates epicyclic gearing to provide forward and reverse rotation of the output shaft. The forward and reverse members of the epicyclic gearing are selectively held by air-operated band brakes (see page 138) which are of a special double-lap type and require no setting or adjustment. An automatic safety device is incorporated in the unit which prevents a change of direction being selected whilst the train is in motion. Lubrication is provided by two gear-type pumps, the output pump operating in both directions of rotation.

This bi-directional gearbox has proved very successful on the U.T.A. multi-purpose diesel cars and does of course ensure that the final drives on the axles are of simplified design whilst eliminating altogether the sliding dog-clutch.

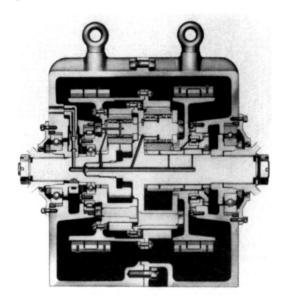

Fig. 113. S.C.G. Type RRE 1 Reversing Gearbox.

CHAPTER ELEVEN

BRAKES

AMONG BRAKING SYSTEMS there are some peculiar to diesel units and with this in view it has been decided to introduce notes covering systems likely to be encountered by readers in the course of their duties with multiple-units and locomotives.

On diesel units the necessary vacuum is created by rotary pumps (exhausters) driven by electric motors, the diesel engine or from the transmission line. The work of the exhauster is indentical with that of the vacuum pump and ejector on a steam locomotive.

RAILCAR EXHAUSTER (*See Fig.* 114)

Generally, two Clayton Dewandre rotary exhausters are used with each power car and are belt-driven from the input side of the gearbox. A non-return valve is fitted between the exhausters and brake pipe to prevent loss of vacuum from the system when the exhausters are stationary. In addition, a filter is provided to prevent dirt from the brake system being drawn into the exhausters which are mounted so as to permit a flow of air over them and ensure efficient cooling when operating for long continuous periods.

This exhauster is a rotary sliding-valve type pump and is not fitted with a snifting valve as the Railcar Quick Release Brake System incorporates a feed valve. The main parts of the exhauster are the body (1), the rotor (2), the heavy-duty bearings (3) and the spring-loaded sealing plates (5). The rotor carries six blades (4) and rotates about its axis which is eccentric to the bore of the body. The volume of space between the blades, rotor and body thus increases and decreases as rotation occurs. An inlet port connected to the vacuum reservoir is situated on the side where the spaces are increasing and an exhaust or outlet port on the side where they are decreasing, so that the air is drawn in at low pressure and expelled at a higher (atmospheric) pressure.

The ends of the exhauster body are sealed off by sealing plates (5) loaded axially by means of the small springs (6) housed in the pockets of the end covers (7).

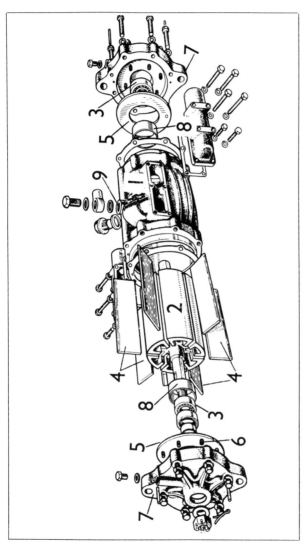

Fig. 114. Exploded view of railcar exhauster. (Clayton Dewandre.)

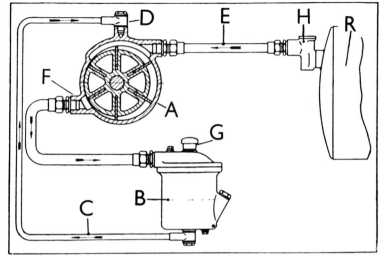

Fig. 115. Exhauster Lubricating System.

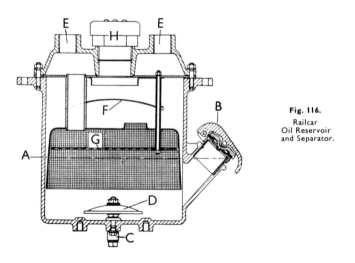

Fig. 116.
Railcar
Oil Reservoir
and Separator.

162

At normal speeds the blades are kept in contact with the bore by centrifugal force but at low speeds particularly when the oil is cold, the blades have insufficient centrifugal force to keep them in their true motion. This is overcome by the action of the cam rings (8) at each end of the rotor which contact the inside edges of the blades and force them to move out radially in their grooves to maintain contact with the bore.

Efficient operation of the exhauster depends upon sufficient oil being supplied to the bearings and also the bore to provide an effective seal between the outer edges of the blades and the bore of the body. A self-contained lubricating system (Fig. 115) enables the exhauster (A) to draw oil from a separator and reservoir unit (B) via the pipe (C). The oil inlet connection (D) is situated at the top of the exhauster body and communicates with the end covers by means of a cross drilling

The vacuum created in the end covers is utilised to pull oil into the exhauster from the separator unit and it is discharged (together with the air evacuated from the brake system via pipe (E)) through the exhauster outlet port (F) and piped into the separator, which retains the oil whilst permitting the air to pass to atmosphere through breather (G).

The oil separator unit (Fig. 116) combines an oil reservoir and filters. The correct oil level (A) up to the filler plug on the side (B) must be maintained in the oil container. The lubrication system utilises suction created by the exhauster to draw oil from the bottom outlet connection (C) through the lower filter (D) and then passes it into the exhauster to lubricate all components.

The ejected oil and the air exhausted from the brake system is returned to the separator unit through one of the large pipe connections (C) in the top cover. A series of baffle plates (F) and the top filter (G) separate the oil from the air and the former falls to the reservoir to complete circulation whilst the air passes to atmosphere via the breather (H) thus relieving pressure in the system. On twin-engined railcars the usual practice is to provide a single separator for both exhausters.

LOCOMOTIVE EXHAUSTER (*See Fig.* 117)

The principle of the Northey Rotary vacuum pump differs radically from most others. Two balanced rotors mounted on parallel shafts within the body rotate within a working chamber shaped like a figure "8". At one end of the shafts they are geared together to maintain correct relationship between the rotors. There are no valves and the air flow is controlled by the movement of the rotors past passages in the end covers. The rotors have no actual rubbing contact with each other or the walls of the chamber.

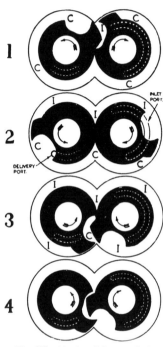

In *Position* 1 the Delivery (left-hand) Rotor "tip" has swept out the Induction Rotor "gap", a partial vacuum has been created in space I which materially assists the induction from the Vacuum Brake Train Pipe just about to commence. Compression of air already removed from the train pipe is commencing in space C.

Position 2 shows delivery commencing to atmosphere from space C through the rapidly opening delivery port, whilst induction is well advanced in space I.

In *Position* 3 induction is complete and the inlet port is shut off from space I whilst delivery is also now complete. A small portion of air removed from the train pipe is trapped in space C.

Position 4 illustrates the "changeover" position—the seal between the rotors is broken freeing the small amount of undelivered air which expands into the rotor chamber. The cycle now recommences at Position 1. During the transition period from Position 4 to Position 1 when the rotors "mesh", the inlet and delivery ports are closed thus isolating the train pipe from atmosphere.

Fig. 117. Northey Exhauster Cycle.
(The inlet port is connected to the vacuum trainpipe, whilst the delivery port discharges via a silencer to atmosphere.)

METCALFE-OERLIKON LOCOMOTIVE BRAKE (*See Fig.* 118.)

The system is termed "vacuum-controlled straight air brake", and is fitted to a considerable number of main-line diesel locomotives. The driver's direct air brake valve is used when shunting or running light. In addition, a driver's vacuum brake valve is fitted for controlling vacuum fitted trains and when using this valve the air brakes of the locomotive are applied automatically and proportionally at the same time. The equipment

164

includes a "fitted-unfitted" selector switch for controlling the *locomotive* brake application (and release times) to suit trains of fitted or unfitted stock.

MAIN AIR EQUIPMENT

Fig. 118 illustrates the principal items of equipment, the compressed air pipe being shown *white*. The electrically-driven compressor (A) charges from the atmosphere via a Suction Strainer and Silencer (B), feeds air to the Main Reservoir (C) through a Drip Cup (D) and Non-Return Valve (E). The purpose of the drip cup is to extract dust and water. Piped directly to the main reservoir is a Safety Valve (F) and a Compressor Governor (G) which is in effect a pressure switch set to start the compressor when the main reservoir drops to 85 lbs. p.s.i. and stop it when the pressure reaches 100 lbs. p.s.i.

On leaving the main reservoir, air is piped via a further drip cup (H) to serve the locomotive's Main Reservoir Pipe from which air is taken for all items of equipment calling for air pressure. A Duplex Check Valve (I) is incorporated to prevent loss of pressure in the event of a Main Reservoir Equalisation Pipe hose becoming damaged or broken. This valve is set at 75 lbs. p.s.i. and is the minimum pressure to which the main reservoir would be allowed to fall by this valve, but under normal circumstances when working locomotives in multiple the air flows through this valve either way and thus maintains equal main reservoir pressure on both locomotives.

AUTOMATIC VACUUM BRAKE

Vacuum pipes are shown *black* in Fig. 118. The electrically-driven exhausters (K) fitted with Silencers (L) draw straight on the vacuum train pipe through the Filter (M) which contains a Check Valve and Relief Valve set to train pipe Vacuum. An isolating cock is provided on each exhauster so that should either unit become faulty it can be isolated. Both exhausters are running at normal speed for maintaining train pipe vacuum.

Each driving cab is equipped with a Driver's Vacuum Brake Valve (J) which has one pipe connection only, direct into the Vacuum Train Pipe. Two switches are contained in this valve, one for speeding up the exhauster and, at the same time opening the Choke Valve when the handle is in RELEASE position. A second switch controls the Cut-Out Valve, closing it in the braking position. On some classes of locomotives a Choke Valve only is fitted and it serves to reduce the area through which the exhausters evacuate the train pipe so enabling emergency brake application such as Automatic Warning System and Deadman to be more effective then they would otherwise be.

When it is desired to release the brakes after an application, both exhausters are speeded up to their maximum by the previously mentioned switch in the driver's vacuum brake valve.

The vacuum brake valve (J) is fitted with a LAP position, may be operated exactly as a conventional vacuum brake valve and when hauling vacuum fitted trains it will apply both the vacuum brakes on the train and the air brakes on the locomotive.

DEADMAN'S EQUIPMENT

The Deadman's Valve (Z) is tapped into the vacuum train pipe and when operated allows air to enter this pipe thus applying both train and locomotive brakes. The Deadman's Pilot Valve (1) controlled by the Reverser Master Handle in the cab, is an isolating device and the air supply to the Deadman's Valve is cut off when the reverser handle is placed in "Engine Only" or "Off" position. However, when the handle is in the "Forward" or "Reverse" position and the deadman's pedal in the cab is released, electric current to the coil in the Valve (Z) is cut off and air enters the valve from the pilot valve (1) in the Controller. This air commences to fill a "timing chamber" attached to valve (Z) and after 6–7 seconds sufficient pressure has been built up to operate the valve and admit air to the vacuum train pipe thus applying the locomotive and train brakes. On depressing the deadman's pedal the reverse action takes place in valve (Z), current is re-established, the train pipe sealed and the timing chamber exhausted once more. The Engine Control Cut-Out Cock (2) is operated by the Reverser in the cab.

LOCOMOTIVE AUTOMATIC BRAKE

Two Triple Valves (O) are fitted on the locomotive and connected to the vacuum train pipe being thus sensitive to any change in vacuum within this pipe caused by the driver's vacuum brake valve or other means (e.g. A.T.C., Deadman, etc., all of which couple into this pipe). Each triple valve is supplied with air from the auxiliary reservoir (P) which in turn is fed from the main reservoir. A Check Valve (Q) is provided to protect the auxiliary reservoir and ensure that, even if for reasons unforeseen the main reservoir lost most of its air, there would be sufficient brake applications available in reserve unaffected by any such losses.

On placing the handle of the Driver's Vacuum Brake Valve (J) to BRAKE ON the drop in vacuum in the train pipe causes the triple valves to pass air to the Bogie Brake Cylinders (R). Similarly, when the valve handle is returned to RUNNING or RELEASE, increase in the train pipe vacuum will cause the triple valves to release air from the brake cylinders. The build-up and release of air pressure in the brake cylinders is directly proportional to the reduction or increase in train pipe vacuum. Two triple valves are fitted in order to ensure rapid filling or release times of the brake cylinders as well as to provide a safety factor.

DIRECT AIR BRAKE

Each driving cab is fitted with a Driver's Direct Air Brake Valve (S) which serves the bogie brake cylinders (R) only and is used solely when

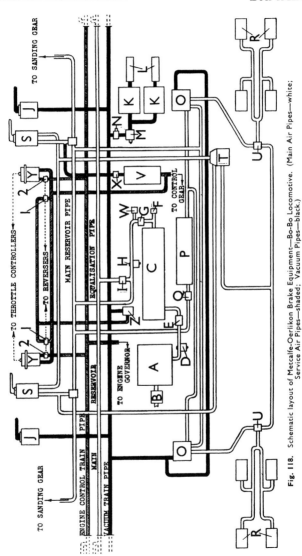

Fig. 118. Schematic layout of Metcalfe-Oerlikon Brake Equipment—Bo-Bo Locomotive. (Main Air Pipes—white; Service Air Pipes—shaded; Vacuum Pipes—black.)

167

the locomotive is on shunting duties. This Direct air brake valve, used in conjunction with Relay Valve (T), serves both bogies and is designed to give step-by-step application and release—no LAP position exists. When the brake handle is in the full BRAKE ON position the maximum brake cylinder pressure will result. Brake power to the bogie is fed through flexible hoses supplying Automatic and Direct air brake power respectively and each of these feed pipes enter one side of a Double Check Valve (U) which enables the air pressure served by one or other pipe (according to the particular driver's brake valve—J or S—being used) to feed the groups of brake cylinders.

CONTROL AIR EQUIPMENT

The air pressure required for operating the electro-pneumatic switch-gear—"control air"—is taken from a special Reservoir (V) which is maintained at a constant pressure by the Pressure Reducing Valve (X). The control reservoir also serves the deadman's valve and Diesel Engine Governor.

CONTROL CIRCUIT GOVERNOR

A Control Circuit Governor (W) is installed in the main air line from the main reservoir and a pressure switch is set to cut off power to the traction motors when the main reservoir pressure drops below a certain figure. This switch has a differential of 15 lbs. p.s.i. and its purpose is to prevent normal movement of the locomotive before the main reservoir is adequately filled.

THROTTLE CONTROL

To vary the speed of the diesel engine a special valve known as the Engine Accelerator Valve (Y) is cam-worked by the throttle controller in the cab and when operating locomotives in multiple the diesel engines of several units can be kept at identical revs.

SERVICE AIR

Certain pipes on Fig. 118 are shaded, these may be described as Service Air. Apart from the Control Reservoir for switchgear, such pipes provide a supply to operate the pneumatic control of certain valves. The air flow in these pipes is very low.

OTHER FEATURES

Under certain conditions, the adhesion of the locomotive's wheels to the rails can be improved by the partial application of the locomotive brakes. By pressing a push-button switch in the cab the driver will cause an

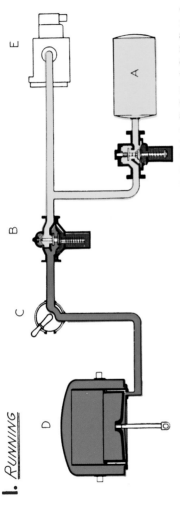

The illustration shows the equipment in the RUNNING position with the car in motion and the exhauster operating at maximum speed. The function of the feed valve (**B**) is to prevent the train pipe vacuum rising above 21 ins. To do this it does not admit air like an ordinary relief valve but shuts down altogether at the required train pipe vacuum thus isolating the exhauster from the rest of the system. The exhauster then creates its maximum vacuum, say 27 ins. or 28 ins. in the release chamber (**A**), which gives storage capacity for subsequent brake releases.

The feed valve consists of a rubber-seated valve normally held off its seat by a powerful spring to which is opposed a large rubber diaphragm, this diaphragm is open to atmosphere on the underside and in communication with the train pipe on the opposite side. At 21 ins. vacuum the upward force on the diaphragm overcomes the spring loading and shuts the valve.

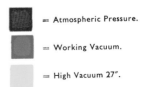

= Atmospheric Pressure.

= Working Vacuum.

= High Vacuum 27".

Fig. 119. Quick Release Vacuum Brake—
Running Position.

Fig. 120 shows the driver's valve (C) in the LAP position (which it passes through on the movement of the handle towards brake-on position) isolating the feed valve (B) and exhauster (E) before air is admitted to the train pipe and thereby preserving the high vacuum conditions in the release chamber (A).

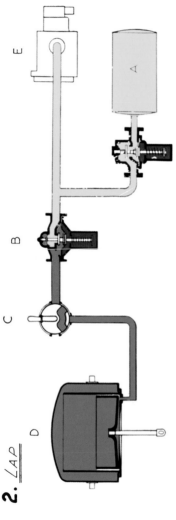

Fig. 120. Quick Release Vacuum Brake—
—Lap Position.

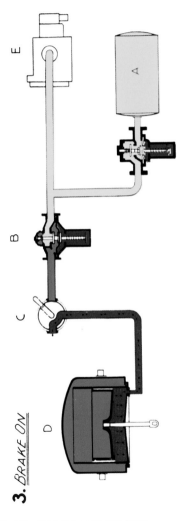

Fig. 121 shows the BRAKE-ON position with air admitted direct to the cylinder (**D**) to apply the brake and the high vacuum still preserved in the release chamber (**A**). Partial applications can be maintained by returning the handle to the LAP position.

Recent tests have shown that a full brake application on a two-car diesel set can be released in a matter of six seconds.

Figs. 122 and 123 overleaf illustrate the brake release action of the Gresham type A.I.V. Quick Release System.

= Atmospheric Pressure.

= Working Vacuum.

= High Vacuum 27″.

Fig. 121 Quick Release Vacuum Brake—
Brake On position.

171

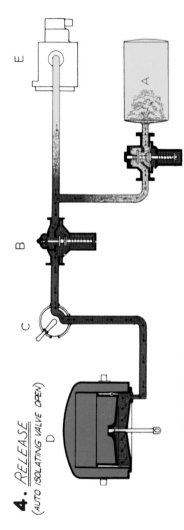

Fig. 122 illustrates the brake in the RELEASE position with the automatic isolating valve open. The driver's brake valve (C) now links the train pipe with the release chamber (A) via the feed valve (B) which opens to its full extent due to loss of vacuum above its diaphragm.

Air from below the vacuum brake piston and from the train pipe flows rapidly through the feed valve into the release chamber which is of ample volume to absorb all the air in the system.

Immediately 21 ins. is reached on the train pipe side of the feed valve the latter closes as before. It will be appreciated that the speed at which the exhausters are running has no bearing on the speed of the brake release which *is entirely dependent on the release chamber*. It is thus possible to release a full brake application in a few seconds, even though the engines and exhausters are at idling speed. The driver's brake handle then remains in this position and full release vacuum is re-created in the release chamber when the car is again in motion and the exhausters running at full capacity.

Atmospheric Pressure.

Working Vacuum.

High Vacuum 27″.

Fig. 122. Quick Release Vacuum Brake— Release Position—A.I.V. Open.

172

Fig. 123 shows the brake RELEASE when the A.I.V. is closed. The air is now being withdrawn from the underside of the brake cylinder by the exhausters, the system functioning in the same way as the orthodox vacuum brake.

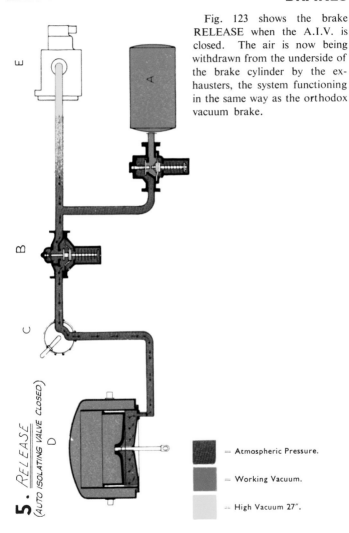

= Atmospheric Pressure.

= Working Vacuum.

= High Vacuum 27″.

Fig. 123. Quick Release Vacuum Brake— Release Position—A.I.V. closed.

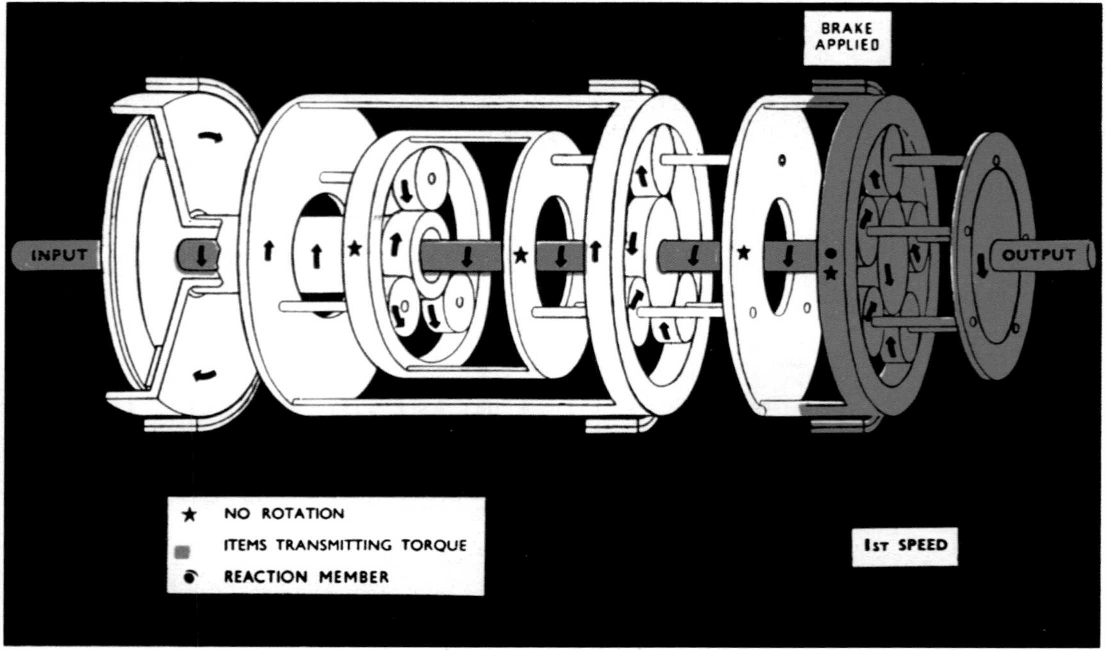

BRAKE
APPLIED

OUTPUT

INPUT

1ST SPEED

★ NO ROTATION

■ ITEMS TRANSMITTING TORQUE

● REACTION MEMBER

Fig. 124. Self-Change Gearbox torque transmission diagram—1st speed.

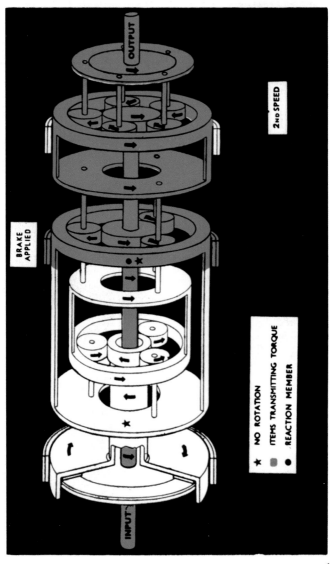

NO ROTATION

ITEMS TRANSMITTING TORQUE

REACTION MEMBER

BRAKE APPLIED

2ND SPEED

OUTPUT

INPUT

Fig. 125. Self-Change Gearbox torque transmission diagram—2nd speed

175

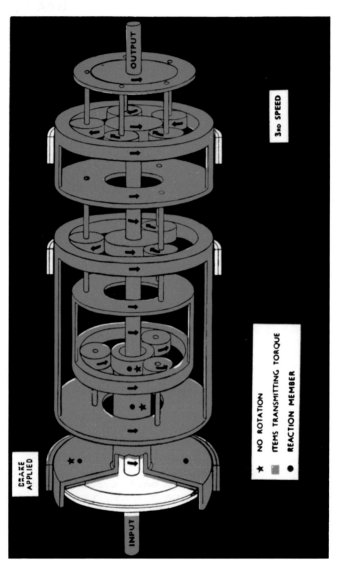

OUTPUT

3RD SPEED

BRAKE APPLIED

INPUT

★ NO ROTATION

▨ ITEMS TRANSMITTING TORQUE

● REACTION MEMBER

Fig. 126. Self-Change Gearbox torque tranmission diagram—3rd speed

176

electro-pneumatic valve to operate the triple valves and pass a brake cylinder pressure not exceeding 15 lbs. p.s.i. During this "Anti-Slip" application wheel slip is avoided whilst the locomotive speed may be increased. It is customary to release the locomotive brakes whilst still holding on the train brake as a means of stretching the train and as an aid to uncoupling. This is achieved through the medium of a driver's switch, an E.P. Valve and the triple valves. From the foregoing it will be appreciated that the air compressor and vacuum exhausters of the locomotive are driven by individual electric motors and are therefore completely independent of engine or transmission speed.

RAILCAR QUICK RELEASE VACUUM BRAKE

With the diesel car standing in a station, gear selector in neutral and engines idling, the freewheel shaft will be revolving at idling speed and thus the belt-driven exhausters will be at their minimum speed, all of which means that the capacity required to release the brakes *quickly* will not be available.

The Gresham & Craven Quick Release A.I.V. System is designed to ensure quick release of the brakes irrespective of the exhauster speed and this is achieved through the medium of a separate "release chamber" which is charged to a high degree of vacuum whilst the car is running. In this system an automatic isolating valve (A.I.V.) is interposed between the release pipe and the high vacuum release chambers on each car, and this valve closes when the vacuum in the release chamber falls to 19 ins. This action prevents the vacuum in the release chamber from falling below a useful value, particularly when several brake applications and releases are made in quick succession without allowing time for complete re-charging of the high vacuum side. The automatic isolating valve allows air to be withdrawn freely from the release chamber, but controls the flow back into the chamber, closing altogether when admission of further air would destroy its effectiveness. The valve thus reduces to minimum the volume which has to be dealt with by the exhausters alone when high vacuum is not available to assist release.

There are several additional important advantages with this system, one of which is that when coupling railcars together or uncoupling for single unit operation, only the exhauster pipes have to be re-charged in addition to the train pipe, before the brakes can be released, thus saving considerable time. The main features of the system are shown in simple form in Fig. 119 and comprise the Exhauster (E), a high vacuum Release Chamber (A), a Feed Valve (B), two-pipe driver's Brake Valve (C), standard Vacuum Brake Cylinder (D) and an automatic isolating valve.

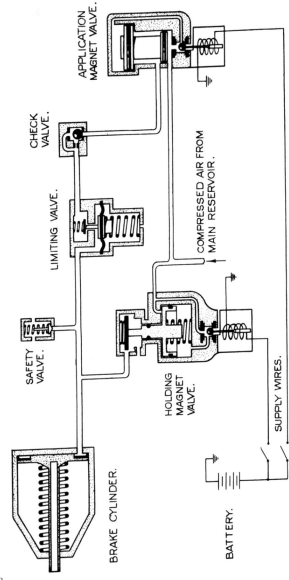

APPLICATION MAGNET VALVE.

CHECK VALVE.

LIMITING VALVE.

COMPRESSED AIR FROM MAIN RESERVOIR.

SAFETY VALVE.

HOLDING MAGNET VALVE.

SUPPLY WIRES.

BRAKE CYLINDER.

BATTERY.

Fig. 127.   Diagram of simple E.P. Brake.

ELECTRO-PNEUMATIC BRAKE

We have dealt with air and vacuum brakes but have not touched on the E.P. brake—an important subject particularly as the Westinghouse self-lapping E.P. brake is fitted to the diesel-electric Pullman trains operating on the London Midland and Western Regions. As is well known these trains are made up of either six or eight cars and the Westinghouse E.P. brake employed combines under the control of a single handle (a) the E.P. brake which is an electrically-controlled compressed air brake and the normal service brake; (b) the automatic brake which is the standard "Westinghouse Automatic brake" providing emergency application either by the driver, the guard, the passengers or in the event of the train parting. It can be used for service stops ir required; (c) the high-speed brake which is an additional automatic feature. We will deal with each of the three sections separately.

E.P. BRAKE

A diagram of a simple E.P. brake is shown in Fig. 127 and the following is the sequence of operations. When the controller handle is in the "Release" position, both the Holding and Application magnet valve circuits are open and the valves are in the positions shown. The brake cylinder is open to atmosphere through the Holding magnet valve. The compressed air supply is isolated from the brake cylinder by the closed Application magnet valve.

When the brake is to be applied, the controller handle is turned; the first movement of the handle closes the Holding magnet valve circuit energising the magnet valve to close the brake cylinder exhaust. Further handle movement energises the Application magnet valve to open and admit compressed air from the supply to the brake cylinder.

When the brake cylinder reaches the desired value, the Application magnet valve is de-energised to cut off the flow of compressed air to the brake cylinder, but the Holding magnet valve remains energised to retain brake cylinder pressure.

Graduated operation of the E.P. brake is available for both application and release and the self-lapping feature of the brake permits a dummy cylinder pressure both in application and release, dependent on the degree of handle movement within the E.P. range of the driver's brake valve. The actual brake cylinder pressure, however, is dependent on whether or not the high speed brake is in operation.

AUTOMATIC BRAKE

The Westinghouse Automatic brake is operated by varying the air pressure in the brake pipe and is shown on page 181 in diagram form. The brake is applied by *releasing* air from the brake pipe to exhaust and released by *restoring* the air pressure in the brake pipe. The brake is normally applied by train crew (or passengers in an emergency) but rupture of a hose coupling or any considerable escape of air from the brake pipe will immediately apply the brake—hence the term "automatic". The driver's control in the driving position is virtually a cock and a relay valve (equalising discharge valve) which either admits air or releases it from the train pipe. Compressed air from the main supply is reduced to a pre-determined constant pressure by a reducing valve and passes through the driver's control valve to the brake pipe. From the brake pipe, which is continuous throughout the length of the train, the air passes to a triple valve and auxiliary reservoir on each vehicle.

Application is made by operating the brake controller to *reduce* the pressure in the equalising reservoir which in turn causes the pressure in the brake pipe to be reduced through the medium of the equalising discharge valve. The reduction of pressure in the brake pipe causes the triple valves to operate and allow air to flow from the auxiliary reservoirs to the dummy cylinders thereby causing the brakes to apply via the booster valves. Release of the brakes is achieved by restoring the air pressure in the brake pipe thus causing the triple valves to vent the dummy cylinders to atmosphere and allow the auxiliary reservoirs to be recharged to brake pipe pressure. When the E.P. brake is in use the Automatic brake is not applied but remains with the brake pipe and auxiliary reservoirs charged, ready for use in emergency. For emergency applications with the brake controller the E.P. brake will apply in addition to the automatic brake.

HIGH-SPEED BRAKE

When an application is made at low speeds (irrespective of the method) compressed air is admitted to the dummy cylinders. At low speeds the pressure in the dummy cylinders registers on one piston (main control piston) of the booster valves, one of which is provided on each car. These booster valves, acting as relay valves, allow air to pass into the brake cylinders from the supplementary reservoirs until the pressure in the brake cylinders is the same as in the dummy cylinder. The supplementary reservoirs—one provided for each booster valve—are charged with air from the main reservoir pipe. Any change in pressure in the dummy cylinders is immediately reproduced in the brake cylinders by the booster valves.

When the train exceeds a certain speed a high-speed brake control relay, sensitive to track speed and fitted on each motor car, energises a train wire which in turn energises a high-speed brake magnet valve on each car. Should the brake be applied under this condition, the air pressure in the dummy cylinders registers on *two* pistons (main control and secondary

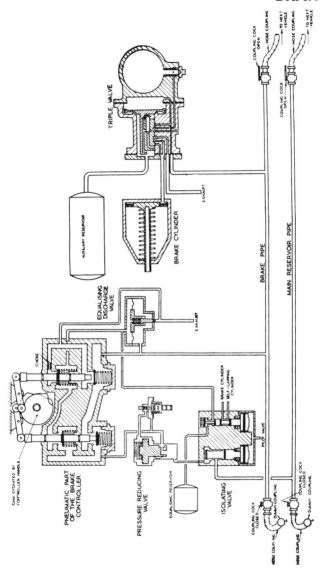

Fig. 128. Diagram of Westinghouse Automatic Brake.

control pistons) of the booster valves instead of only one and an increased brake cylinder pressure is obtained. When the speed of the train falls below a pre-determined value the speed sensitive control relay breaks the circuit to the train wire thus de-energising the high-speed magnet valves, and pressure is then exhausted from the secondary control piston of the booster valve which reduces the brake cylinder pressure to the same pressure as that in the dummy cylinder.

BRAKE CONTROLLERS

Each driving cab is fitted with a brake controller in which all the necessary fittings for controlling both the E.P. and Automatic brakes are mounted on a common pipe bracket. Selection between the brakes is obtained (Fig. 129) by using positions I and II for the E.P. brake and positions I, III, and IV for the Automatic brake. Position V is the "Emergency" position where both E.P. and Automatic brakes are applied together. Position VI—when incorporated—is the "shutdown" position and brake controllers in unoccupied driving compartments are normally locked in this position permitting the handle to be moved to "Emergency" position V only.

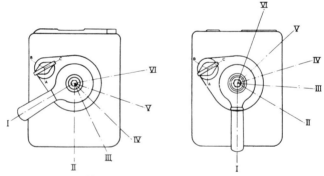

Fig. 129. Types F1 (left) and F3 Brake Controllers.

The E.P. brake controller is virtually an electrical switch operated by the handle increment and by brake cylinder pressure as far as the E.P. brake is concerned and when the driver turns the controller handle to control the brakes the controller connects the train wires to a battery in sequence and thereby energises the magnet valves of an E.P. brake unit on each car. The magnet valves admit air to, and release air from, a dummy cylinder. The resulting pressure in the dummy cylinder is reproduced in the brake cylinders themselves by the action of a booster valve on each car as previously explained. A main reservoir pipe is continuous throughout the train and all E.P. brake units are connected to and fed with compressed air from this pipe.

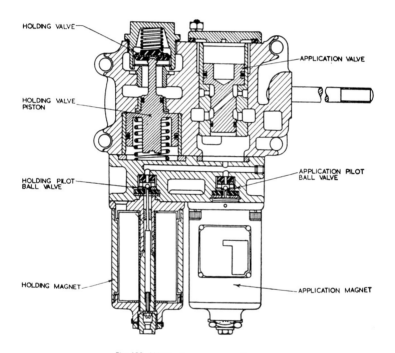

HOLDING VALVE

APPLICATION VALVE

HOLDING VALVE
PISTON

HOLDING PILOT
BALL VALVE

APPLICATION PILOT
BALL VALVE

HOLDING MAGNET

APPLICATION MAGNET

Fig. 130. Westinghouse magnet valve unit.

CHAPTER TWELVE

CONTROLS

THIS IS AN INVOLVED subject and to attempt to describe complete control systems in detail would require more space than this small volume allows, therefore, a diesel-electric locomotive, a diesel-mechanical railcar and a diesel-hydraulic railcar have been used to illustrate several points. There are numerous variations of the systems briefly described and in addition, many other completely different types. The selected examples are however, typical of British practice today and will most likely be encountered by readers.

LOCO. BASIC ELECTRIC CIRCUITS

In the schematic illustration opposite the basic electric circuits of a twin-engined diesel-electric locomotive mounted on two three-axle bogies are seen. In this particular instance all six axles are driven.

Power is taken from each diesel engine to drive (a) the radiator fan, (b) the main generator and (c) the auxiliary generator.

The main generators supply power to a section of each of the control cubicles where, by means of contactors and reversing switches, the power is passed to the traction motors. Each of the traction motors in one bogie is connected in series with another traction motor in the other bogie and the three pairs of series-connected motors thus formed are connected in parallel.

Either master controller controls pneumatically the speed of both diesel engines and thus controls the output of the main generators. The air connections are shown by the dotted lines between the controllers and the governors of the engines.

The auxiliary generators supply power at constant voltage to the control cubicles, and by means of contactors, relays and switches, provide power to drive the fuel supply pumps, traction motor blowers, the compressor, the exhausters, the C.W.A. boiler and for charging the battery, the current from which is used for starting the engines and for the lights.

If one engine is cut out, the power is reduced, but the method of operation remains exactly the same.

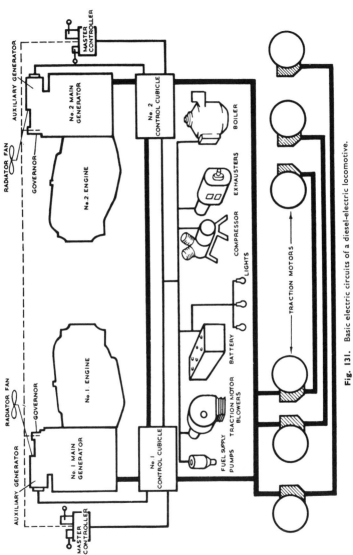

Fig. 131. Basic electric circuits of a diesel-electric locomotive.

185

K

DIESEL-ELECTRIC CONTROL

Two handy methods of controlling the output of the electric generator are available—firstly by varying the speed of the armature and secondly, by altering the amount of current flowing through the coils of the electro-magnets. The former is achieved by varying the governor setting of the diesel (see page 33) and the latter by insertion of a variable resistance in the field system. Both these adjustments are made simultaneously when the driver moves his control handle.

In Fig. 132 will be seen the method employed to inter-relate the functions of the engine governor and a motor-driven resistance regulator. The motor (RM) has two field windings (F1 and F2) and the direction of rotation of the motor is decided by which of the fields is energised. As we already know from page 33, the flyweights of the governor are the initiating components and they act directly on a pilot valve (25) controlling oil admission or discharge to or from servo cylinder (9). Servo (9) is in turn connected by means of the linkage shown to the fuel control rocker (27)—included in the linkage is a spring-loaded telescopic unit (19).

Normal action of the linkage takes place as piston (9) rises and ultimately fuel control rocker (27) falls at its right end until finally stopped by the limit-stop (28)—further upward movement of the piston will compress the spring (19) and close electrical contacts (VLS), which then energise relay (VLR) and the motor (RM) will rotate anti-clockwise, weakening the field (GF) of main generator (G) by the introduction of variable resistance (R).

Unloading of the diesel engine will allow pilot valve (25) to release the oil from servo motor (9) and the piston will fall thus breaking contacts (VLS) and closing contacts (VRS) causing reversal of motor (RM) and increasing main generator excitation until correct engine speed is achieved —whereupon both contacts will be open.

A further refinement in d.e. control is the weakening of the *traction motor* fields (Fig. 133) necessary when, with the loco or railcar accelerating, full excitation of the main generator is reached and full engine power cannot be absorbed. In order to remedy this, the fields of the traction motors are weakened by connecting the contactor resistances (FW) in parallel with the field windings of the motors.

Now, once more, further excitation of the main generator field is possible, and with it further acceleration of the loco. This procedure may be repeated two or three times as further weakening of the traction motor fields is arranged.

LOCOMOTIVE CAB (DIESEL-ELECTRIC)

The simplicity of driving controls of diesel-electrics is one of the attractions of this system and *major* control equipment in the compartment illustrated consists of only two items—a controller and power brake. The controller includes a reverser and a dead-man's pedal is also employed.

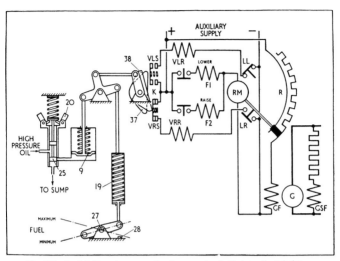

Fig. 132. English Electric system of main generator field-strength variation.

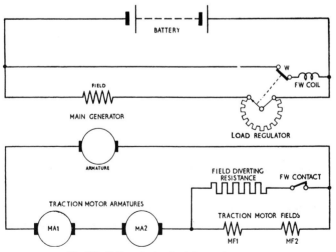

Fig. 133. Field weakening circuit for traction motors.

The other items of cab equipment are normal—a horn or whistle cord, control switches for cab and code lights, wipers, etc., instrument panels complete with warning lights together with vacuum, air gauges and speedometer.

The master controller (Fig. 134) (8) has a removable key and two operating handles—the reverser (6) and the power handle (7).

The straight air brake (2) and vacuum brake (1) are at the driver's left hand whilst the duplex vacuum gauge (4) is situated immediately in front of him. If it is desired to release the loco. air brakes while still maintaining the vacuum brakes on the train, the air-brake cylinder cut-out switch (3) is depressed. The loco. air brakes will remain released as long as the button is kept depressed. The air brake cylinder gauge (5) indicates the two bogies' cylinder pressures.

As the brakes, sanding gear and visible indicators appear in normal railway practice it is the controller as the item of "new" equipment that we must examine. A controller with the inspection cover removed is illustrated in Fig. 135 and this English Electric unit is employed to regulate the voltage to the traction motors and other equipment in a *fixed sequence*. Briefly, the controller consists of three groups of cams controlling the opening and closing of silver-butt contacts energising the operating coils of the solenoids, relays and contactors forming part of the control equipment. The master switch, reverser and engine control each operate through the medium of a handle and these are mechanically interlocked to prevent incorrect use. For instance, the engine control can be moved only when the master switch is in the "ON" position, the reverser in the "FORWARD" or "REVERSE" position and the dead-man's pedal depressed. The master switch handle fits into the socket shown in Fig. 135 and until this is inserted and turned to the "ON" location the controls are "dead". Likewise, the master switch can only be placed in position or removed when the engine control is in "OFF". There is, however, another position for the master switch known as "Engine Only" (E.O.) where it locks the reverse handle at "OFF" but enables the engine control to be utilised in order to run the diesel for testing without the traction motors being connected. A further position of the master switch handle, "START", completes the starting circuits and connects the battery to the generator for starting the diesel engine.

RAILCAR CAB (DIESEL-MECHANICAL) (*See Fig.* 136)

This control compartment has three main control units, an engine speed controller (9) a gear controller (13) and a vacuum brake valve (15). The engine speed controller incorporates a dead-man's device and the gear controller includes a forward and reverse lever (14) which also acts as a master key. When the master key is operated it cancels the control interlocks and supplies current for the complete control table. These controllers use electricity to control compressed air used for operating

Fig. 134. Driving position of B.R. Type 5 diesel-electric locomotive. (English Electric)

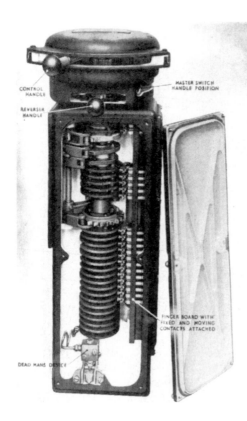

Fig. 135.
Controller
produced
by E.E.Co.
for Main Line
Locomotives.

the throttle motors (Fig. 138-14), the self-change gearboxes (Fig. 138-13) and the forward and reverse mechanisms (Fig. 138-12). This is achieved by means of electro-pneumatic valves, each of which has complete control of particular air lines between the main reservoir and the unit concerned.

DIESEL-MECHANICAL RAILCAR CONTROLS (*See Fig.* 138)

Air is drawn into the system by the two engine-mounted compressors (3) via the air-filter and anti-freezer units (1) and passes by way of non-return valves (5) to the small capacity air reservoir (2) which is fitted with an unloader valve. This initial reservoir enables a rapid build-up of air

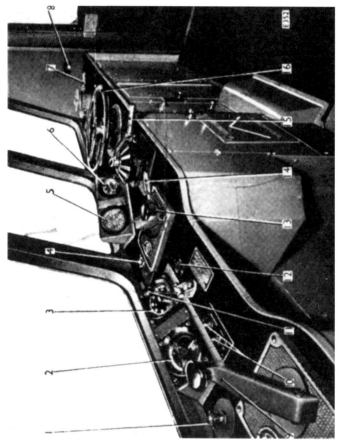

Fig. 136. Driving compartment of B.R. 50,000 Series railcar. (Metro-Cammell)

1. Screen Wiper Control; 2. Engine Speed Indicator; 3. Rail Speed Indicator; 4. Emergency Light Socket; 5. Duplex Vacuum Gauge; 6. Air Pressure Gauge; 7. Guard's Brake Valve; 8. Dead-man's Cancellation Button; 9. Throttle Controller; 10. Panel lights switch (left), Tachometer Change Switch (right); 11. Warning Horns Control; 12. Communication Buzzer; 13. Gear-change Lever; 14. Forward and Reverse Lever; 15. Vacuum Brake; 16. Handbrake.

pressure thus allowing the throttle motor and final drive E.P. valves to be operated.

From the initial reservoir air is supplied to the two main reservoirs (4 & 7) the first of which (4) is equipped with a diverter valve at the inlet end, the purpose of which is to ensure that the primary system (i.e. all the air lines fed from reservoir 2) is fully charged before air is permitted to enter reservoir (4) and beyond. This valve will permit reverse flow of air should for any reason the pressure in the main system fall below that in the secondary reservoir.

Air from the main system passes via an air-pipe filter (6) to a reducing valve (10) which ensures that the pressure is reduced to the lower figure (65 lbs.) required for gearbox piston operation. The nest of gearbox E.P. valves (11) feed the two gearboxes (13)—it should be noted that each one of the E.P. valves feeds two pistons—one in each gearbox. Likewise air from the primary reservoir (4) is taken, via air-pipe filter (6) to the group of E.P.V.s (15) operating the two throttle motors and final drives (14 and 12 respectively). A pipe line from (8) supplies air to the cab pressure gauge and car auxiliaries. Air lines to the coupling cocks and flexible connections between cars are shown in the diagram at (9).

Having already dealt with the pneumatic operation of the gearbox and final drive units in Chapter 10 there remains the throttle motor. A throttle motor is shown in Fig. 139 and this is of the B.U.T. "L" type

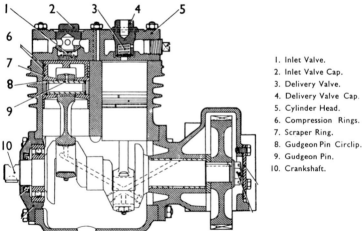

1. Inlet Valve.
2. Inlet Valve Cap.
3. Delivery Valve.
4. Delivery Valve Cap.
5. Cylinder Head.
6. Compression Rings.
7. Scraper Ring.
8. Gudgeon Pin Circlip.
9. Gudgeon Pin.
10. Crankshaft.

Fig. 137. Railcar engine-driven air compressor.

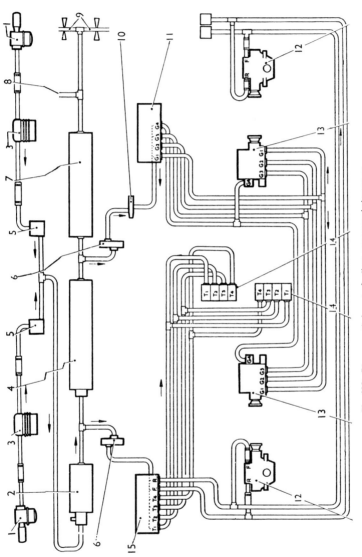

Fig. 138. Diagrammatic layout of railcar compressed-air system.

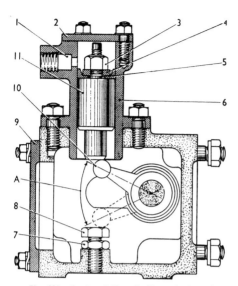

Fig. 139. Sectioned Throttle Motor (end view). B.U.T. "L" type.

which has taken the place of the "A" type motor fitted to B.R. 79000 Series cars and illustrated and described in the first edition of this book. The "L" type motor consists of four air cylinders (one of which is shown (6) in the cross-section) attached to a box section casting. Each cylinder has a combined piston and rod (11) fitted with a synthetic rubber washer or seal (5).

A spindle carried in bushes passes through the length of the box casing and has an operating lever at one end and an alternative lever at the other end which acts as a clamp. Four ball-ended levers (10) are loosely mounted on the spindle together with four bosses which are keyed to the spindle. The connecting faces of the ball-ended levers and bosses are so constructed that any movement of the levers carried out by the action of the air on the piston rotates the spindle, the degree of this movement (A) being limited by four stop-screws (8) set at varying lengths in the bottom of the casting. Air enters the appropriate cylinder, selected by the throttle controller, via the electro-pneumatic valve concerned, through the inlet port (1) and remains pushing the piston down until the controller is moved to another position.

ELECTRO-PNEUMATIC VALVE (*See Fig.* 140)

It will be observed from page 193 that there are ten e.p. valves employed to control the air equipment of the railcar. All these valves are of the "ON" type—that is they will pass air when they are energised ("OFF" type valves are normally passing air and shut when energised). The illustration allows a simple explanation of the operation of an "ON" type valve. The electrical portion of the valve is the lower and the air portion the upper. The solenoid assembly contains an iron core (6)

194

through which passes a brass stem (13) and when the solenoid is energised through its coils (7) the armature (8) is pulled up against the non-magnetic stops (14). This in turn lifts the brass stem (13) which pushes up the air-valve (3) lifting it off its seat (4) against the spring (2), thus allowing compressed air to make its way from the inlet port (10) to the outlet pipe (11) on its way to throttle motor, final drive or gearbox cylinder as the case may be. Valve seat (5) is automatically closed in this position, thus isolating exhaust port (12).

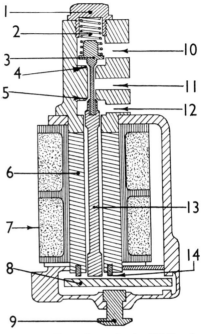

When the solenoid is de-energised, spring (2) forces the valve (3) back on to its seat (4) and thus connects exhaust port (12) to outlet pipe (11) allowing the air in the line to escape to at-

Fig. 140. Electro-Pneumatic valve. ("On" type)

mosphere. A test button (9) is provided for operation manually. The object of the dielectric stops (14) is to provide an air space between the armature (8) and the bottom of the iron core (6), preventing the armature being upheld by residual magnetism.

DIESEL-HYDRAULIC RAILCAR CONTROLS (*See Fig.* 141)

On previous pages we have shown the control system used on diesel-mechanical railcars. Many Rolls-Royce powered diesel-hydraulic cars operate with a Westinghouse pneumatic system for engine and transmission control.

The diagram shows a typical control layout for the engines, torque converters and final drives of a twin-engined railcar. Engine speed is regulated by means of the driver's throttle controller (TV) which meters air from the main reservoir pipe to the throttle pipe from whence it is fed to the actuators (A) which control engine speed proportionally to the handle movement of the throttle control valve. It will be observed that the engine control is therefore purely pneumatic—and this is suitable for the shorter train—the throttle control valve (Fig, 142) provides an air supply the pressure of which can be varied in proportion to the degree of handle movement. A fully automatic feature of the valve ensures that the selected pressure is maintained irrespective of slight leakage. A "deadman's" handle is fitted which also prevents the engine throttles being re-opened unless the handle is first returned to the "OFF" position. The diaphragm type actuators (Fig. 143) mounted on the engines provide a compact and accurate method of regulating the fuel injection pump rack and the travel of the operating arm can be finely adjusted.

To ensure that the speed of the engines widely spaced in a long diesel train are fully synchronised Westinghouse automatic electro-pneumatic throttle assistance is employed. This is comprised of a self-lapping contact unit in the driving cab and two E.P. valves on each car, one E.P. valve to charge and the other to exhaust the through throttle pipe as necessary when accelerating or decelerating the engines. Thus fully graduable, equalised and synchronised speed control is obtained irrespective of the length of the train.

Selection of "direct" or "converter" drive and the operation of the reversing final drives is by means of remotely controlled magnet (e.p.) valves. The operation of the magnet valves is safeguarded by various devices and interlocks which operate to allow air pressure to be applied or released to the appropriate cylinder.

THROTTLE CONTROL VALVE. (*See Fig.* 142)

This Westinghouse unit is constructed in three main sections—the handle mechanism, the body bracket complete with electrical equipment, and the pressure control unit. The handle mechanism consists of a spring loaded "deadmans" lever which, by means of a spring loaded handle return plate, is prevented from being depressed unless it has first been returned to "OFF", should it have been released for any reason.

The main body bracket contains oil retaining bushes which support the operating shaft. Sliding on the operating shaft and operated by a vertical push-rod within the shaft is the spring loaded circular-form "deadmans" cam. Beneath the "deadmans" cam is the range change cam and adjacent to it the detent ring. At the lower end of the operating shaft is the face cam which operates the Pressure Control Unit. The electrical equipment consists of two "snap over" switches; wires from these switches are taken to a separate terminal board.

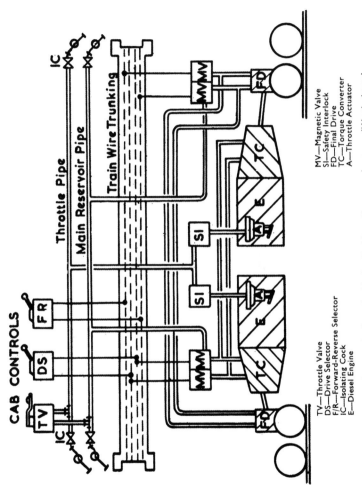

Fig. 141. Diagram of twin-engined hydraulic drive railcar control system. (Westinghouse)

TV—Throttle Valve
DS—Drive Selector
F/R—Forward-Reverse Selector
IC—Isolating Cock
E—Diesel Engine

MV—Magnetic Valve
SI—Safety Interlock
FD—Final Drive
TC—Torque Converter
A—Throttle Actuator

197

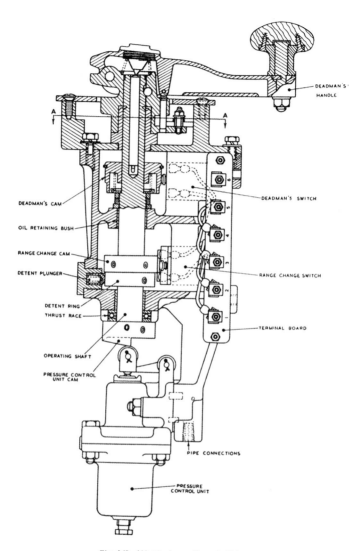

DEADMAN'S HANDLE

DEADMAN'S SWITCH

DEADMAN'S CAM

OIL RETAINING BUSH

RANGE CHANGE CAM

DETENT PLUNGER

RANGE CHANGE SWITCH

DETENT RING
THRUST RACE

TERMINAL BOARD

OPERATING SHAFT

PRESSURE CONTROL
UNIT CAM

PIPE CONNECTIONS

PRESSURE
CONTROL UNIT

Fig. 142. Westinghouse Throttle Valve.

The Pressure Control Unit comprises an upper and a lower portion. The upper portion consists of a combined inlet/exhaust valve assembly, together with the operating lever and roller, and the lower portion houses the diaphragm and control spring. When a force is brought to bear on the operating lever, the inlet/exhaust valve assembly is moved downwards a proportional amount. This movement seats the exhaust valve and then unseats the inlet valve against the pressure of its spring, to allow pressure to flow to the throttle pipe and to the chamber above the diaphragm. The throttle pipe pressure which is present on the top of the diaphragm, is balanced by the effort of the large spring, so that the diaphragm movement is proportional to the pressure. The downward movement of the diaphragm carries with it the exhaust valve seat and, due to the effort of the inlet valve spring, the exhaust and inlet ball. This movement allows the inlet ball to seat, thus retaining the throttle pipe pressure at a figure proportional to the downward movement. In a similar manner, when the force is removed from the operating lever to decrease the throttle pipe pressure, the inlet/exhaust valve assembly moves an amount depending on the operating lever movement. The upward movement of the valve body lifts the exhaust ball off its seat while the inlet ball remains seated due to the pressure of the inlet spring. The excess throttle pipe pressure is thus vented through the opening in the diaphragm chamber to atmosphere, and the diaphragm rises to achieve a new balanced position corresponding to the reduced pressure. The upward movement of the diaphragm continues until the exhaust valve seat closes against the exhaust ball and cuts off further venting.

OPERATION OF WESTINGHOUSE THROTTLE VALVE

With the handle released and in the "OFF" position, the "deadmans" circuit is broken and there is no air supply to the throttle actuators. At this position the spring loaded handle return plate allows the handle to be depressed and the "deadmans" circuit made.

Rotation of the handle towards the IDLING POSITION causes the lower face cam to progressively operate the Pressure Control Unit until 10 p.s.i. air pressure is applied to the throttle actuators by the time the handle is at IDLING; at this position a slight resistance is felt due to the spring loaded detent.

Further handle movement causes a proportional pressure increase until, at a position (indicated by a detent) 10 degrees before FULL THROTTLE, 60 p.s.i. is felt at the throttle actuators which corresponds to full throttle at the engine.

A range-change switch is provided which is operated after the handle passes the "10 degree" detent position. This has the effect of keeping the torque converter in hydraulic drive until a higher track speed has been reached, before changing into direct drive.

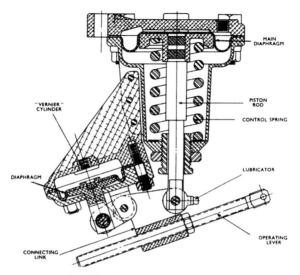

Fig. 143. Westinghouse throttle actuator.

ACTUATOR

This unit performs a similar function to the throttle motor illustrated on page 194. The Westinghouse unit consists of a cast body containing a spring controlled diaphragm, the piston and piston rod. On the side of the Actuator is a pivot point to which the adjustable screwed operating lever is attached and the piston rod also is linked to this lever. The variable pressure air supply from the throttle control valve is connected to one side of the diaphragm and when a pressure of 10 p.s.i. is achieved the pre-loaded spring begins to compress. Thus the piston rod and lever move in proportion to the applied pressure from 10 to 60 p.s.i. when full throttle is achieved. Therefore as the lever is linked to the engine governor the engine speed is varied in proportion to the degree of throttle valve handle movement under the driver's control.

There is a vast field of auxiliary equipment employed with diesel rail units which cannot be dealt with within the confines of this book—batteries, anti-freezers, train heating units, exhaust systems and many others. The reader is recommended to the standard text books available on these subjects if he wishes to delve further.

Several works are available from public libraries and many of them will take the interested reader more deeply into the subject—the present book is by way of being a primer or introduction. Strongly recommended are the following:—

"*Diesel Locomotives and Railcars*", by Reed (Locomotive Publishing Company). The book should be read by all interested in diesel traction.

"*Diesel-Electric Shunting Locomotives*", by Finegan (George Newnes). Contains some most interesting facts and figures gathered from practical experience.

"*The Diesel Locomotive*", by Aston (Thames & Hudson). Recommended particularly to those interested in the diesel-mechanical shunter and line locomotive.

"*The Motor Vehicle*", by Newton & Steeds (Iliffe). Highly recommended to diesel-railcar men for its information on the c.i. oil engine, cooling and exhaust systems, propeller shafts, etc.

"*An Introduction to Diesel-Electric Traction Equipment*", (The English Electric Company Limited). The company's publication TD126 is an invaluable introduction to diesel-electric equipment as applied to rail traction.

"*The High-speed Compression-Ignition Engine*", by Dicksee (Blackie). Written by one of A.E.C.'s outstanding designers and a standard work on this subject. Recommended for the advanced reader.

M.I.C. secretaries should ensure that several excellent 16 mm. sound films are projected for their members, among which may be mentioned "*Diesel on the Rail*", "*British Locomotives*" and "*All Change Gear*"—the first from the Shell Organisation, the second from the Central Office of Information, and the last-named from Self-Changing Gears Ltd. The last two are colour films.

For
Railway
Modernisation

Prominent among new developments for use in railway modernisation schemes are Stone-Vapor boilers and 'Watchman' heaters—for carriage heating and diesel engine pre-heating respectively; Smith-Stone instruments for speed indication, measurement and control; and Stone-Maybach 'Mekydro' power transmissions. These products have all taken their place with other established J. STONE equipments for train lighting, air-conditioning, auxiliary power generation, etc., etc. and already are making substantial contributions to the economic and efficient operation of railways throughout the world.

J. STONE
& CO. (DEPTFORD) LTD.
ARKLOW ROAD, LONDON, S.E.14.

A member of the Stone-Platt Group

STONE - VAPOR BOILER

'WATCHMAN' HEATER

SPEEDOMETER EQUIPMENT

POWER TRANSMISSION

For the Napier 'Deltic'
CUSHYMOUNTS

On the "English Electric" Deltic-powered Type 5 locomotives for British Railways, the most powerful single
unit diesel-electrics in the world, the engine generator
sets are carried on four Metalastik Cushymounts. These
have the same flexibility in all directions and are provided with built-in resilient stops which take
longitudinal shock loads and can be adjusted to limit the
sway of the engine when starting and stopping. The
Cushymount and Cushyfoot 'S' mountings are now used by
a number of leading builders of diesel locomotives in
Britain and overseas and are giving good vibration insulation and trouble-free service. The Cushymount (illustrated) is used for medium and high speed engines with loads
up to 5 tons and deflections up to $\frac{3}{4}$" per mounting point.
The Cushyfoot 'S' is for high speed, lightweight engines. It
supports loads up to $2\frac{1}{2}$ tons with deflections up to $\frac{3}{8}$".

FUEL INJECTION & ELECTRICAL EQUIPMENT

FOR DIESEL LOCOMOTIVES

C.A.V. manufacture fuel injection and electrical equipment for main line, goods, shunting and narrow gauge locomotives, railcars or railbuses. Manufacturing resources are unequalled, and engine manufacturers are offered the benefits of unrivalled facilities for research, design and development. C.A.V. equipment is backed by the world's finest service organisation covering over 100 countries.

150 AMP 24V AC generator totally enclosed type